'... AND NOTHING BUT THE TRUTH'?

by
DEON GOUWS

ZEBRA

Published by Zebra (an imprint of the Struik New Holland
Publishing Group (Pty) Ltd)
PO Box 1144, Cape Town, 8000

First edition, first impression October 2000

10 9 8 7 6 5 4 3 2 1

Publication © Zebra Press 2000
Text © Deon Gouws 2000

PUBLISHING MANAGER Marlene Fryer
EDITOR Kerryn McKay
COVER DESIGNER Beverley Dodd
DTP Beverley Dodd

Reproduction by Hirt & Carter (Pty) Ltd
Printed and bound by CTP Book Printers, Caxton Street, Parow, 7500

ISBN 1 86872 352 6

'... AND NOTHING BUT THE TRUTH'?

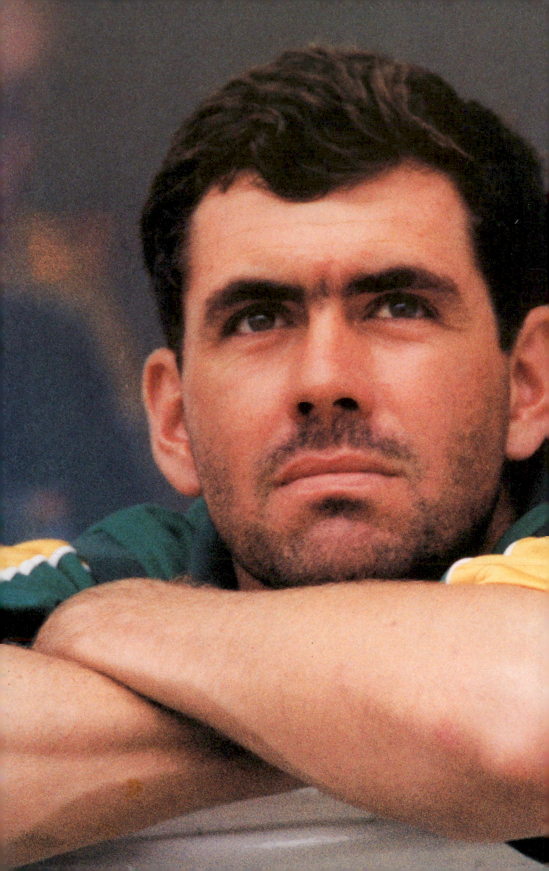

Contents

To my mother, Marie, the fanatic, for the inspiration to write a book on her behalf. Never has Hansie had a greater fan – of course she's forgiven him. I hope she can handle the publicity.

To my late father, Ben, for the love of sport and for all the long stories he used to tell. If you don't learn to tell a long story, you will never fill a book. He had the best memory for unimportant detail I have ever seen – also something that helps fill the pages. And he often reminded me of how I drove him up the wall with my inquisitive mind when I was little. Once again, this book has more questions than it has answers. I hope he can read this where he is.

To my wonderful wife, Naomi, for all her love, support, understanding and patience. I always wanted to dedicate my books to her, but I hope she's happy to share this time. She normally understands these things, which is why she's managed to put up with me for so long.

Introduction

Hansie Cronjé became captain of the South African national cricket team at the end of 1994, just as we were starting to put the finishing touches to our preparations for the 1995 Rugby World Cup. When we eventually won that trophy in front of 65,000 fanatical supporters in Johannesburg some six months later, all of us knew that it was an event we could never forget. For many supporters it was an emotional climax like they'd never experienced before; for most of the players it would turn out to be a highlight, the likes of which they could simply never expect to enjoy again.

The world of professional sport is a lot smaller than most people think. Because of this, I got to know most of the members of the South African cricket team over the years. I therefore also have a pretty good idea of how much our victory in the Rugby World Cup meant to each and every one of them. First and foremost, the members of the cricket team were loyal patriots, not unlike the proverbial man in the street, not unlike the typical holder of a season ticket, not unlike the average fan who is likely to read this book. But in addition to this, they were also contenders who would gain strength in their preparations for the 1996 Cricket World Cup … knowing that their countrymen had done it before … knowing that they too had the potential to take on the world and walk off with the spoils.

They had, after all, presented us with some of those special moments themselves. Who will ever forget the third and final match of the one-day series against India in 1991, when Kepler Wessels, Peter Kirsten and Adrian Kuiper achieved what had seemed impossible, surpassing the opposition's mammoth score of 287 with more than three overs to spare on a hot night in New Delhi? Or the dramatic victory over Australia in Sydney in January 1994, when Fanie de Villiers bowled himself into the record books and the boys from Down Under were dismissed for 111 in the final innings? Not to mention South Africa's first test back at Lord's, the home of cricket, when our team beat the English with 356 runs inside four days, only six months later ...

As it turned out, the 1996 Cricket World Cup was a disappointment for the members of South Africa's cricket team and for all their fans. They were on top of their game all through the build-up, only to come unstuck against the best batsman in the world, on a day when everything simply went his way. I knew how devastated Hansie Cronjé was after that tournament. I knew it because I knew him personally, I knew his athletic prowess, I knew his dedication, and I knew his competitive spirit. But I'm sure the emotions he went through at the time would eventually not compare with his own disappointment about the way in which his career in competitive cricket was destined to end.

I feel sorry for Hansie, the person. How can I not? We have known each other for a long time, and we have shared so many similar experiences. Few people understand the demands of a career in professional sport: demands on your body (remember, you only have one), demands on your family life (if you have one), and demands on your free time (you basically have none).

Whatever happened when things went wrong, and the world of betting became entangled with the world of cricket, can never be condoned. It is important, however, that the truth comes out – not only for the sake of cricket, but indeed in the interest of all professional sport. As a professional rugby player turned full-time rugby administrator, sport has always been my life. Not only that, but sport is also my business, the players are my colleagues, the spectators are my clients. And when we see each other at next Saturday's game, all of us want to look each other in the eye, in the full confidence that there's nothing wrong with the transaction.

That's why the King Commission in South Africa is so important. What it reveals may appear damaging to cricket in the short term, but it will prove crucial to the long-term survival of the sport.

That's also why a book like this makes an important contribution. In searching for the truth, there are always a multitude of possible sources that can be explored. In this book, Deon Gouws combines the views of some of the people who know Hansie best, with insights from people from many other walks of life. Deon's career as an investment professional puts him in a position to make meaningful comparisons between the world of sport and the world of business, for example; his experience also enables him to do statistical analysis of cricket in a way that sets him apart from the typical sports journalist.

I have known Deon since 1986 when I was a first-year student in the Afslaan men's residence at the Rand Afrikaans University; he was a member of the house committee at the time. In that capacity, he had co-responsibility for running a not-too-enjoyable initiation programme which our group of plebs (our official name) had to live through. But we became friends regardless, and we have managed to maintain contact over the years. I've always known Deon to be an achiever of the highest order, a sports-lover of note and a balanced individual with a fine sense of humour. All in all, a combination which qualifies him to contribute an account of the Hansie Cronjé saga which is not only insightful and objective, but also an enjoyable read.

FRANÇOIS PIENAAR
London

20 September 2000

'... there appears to be a perception that this Commission should somehow or other be used or regarded as an instrument of revenge; a vehicle for some sort of witch-hunt. This is quite emphatically not so. I am going to be conducting an inquiry with the purpose as I have indicated of, in the first instance, ascertaining the truth.'

Judge Edwin King, 7 June 2000

Preface

'RUBBISH!' the headline shouted. It was Saturday 8 April 2000. A day earlier, police in Delhi had released transcripts of an alleged telephonic conversation between Cronjé and an Indian businessman named Sanjay Chawla, supposedly a bookie. If the transcripts were genuine, Cronjé would appear guilty of match-fixing, and providing confidential information to outside parties. Four other players were also implicated: Herschelle Gibbs, Pieter Strydom, Henry Williams and Nicky Bojé.

'RUBBISH!' I concurred, quietly sipping my cappuccino whilst reading about what simply had to be a conspiracy against our captain and the four other players.

What an improbable story, I thought. This was Hansie Cronjé, arguably the cleanest character in the world of cricket. An Australian only walks when his car breaks down, someone once told me, but Hansie would always walk when he got a nick. What's more, he was even known to call back a batsman from the opposite team if the player had been given 'out' under dubious circumstances.

Hansie Cronjé's name had franchise value like few others in international cricket. Respected the world over as a great captain, a high-quality all-rounder and a fierce competitor, very few people could believe that he would ever be guilty of unethical behaviour.

Cronjé's future was bright: practically anything that he was happy to attach his name to would have a very good chance of turning out to be a success. He had already signed a number of lucrative endorsement contracts, and none seemed to summarise his character better than the advert for a range of luxury watches, with the pay-off line 'Inner Strength'. Whether he wanted to go into coaching, administration or business, the world was his oyster. Surely he would never risk his tremendous future earning capacity in return for the proverbial fast buck!

What is more, Hansie was a committed Christian. He wore a wrist band inscribed with the letters WWJD, which stands for 'What Would Jesus Do?'. It simply seemed unthinkable that he, of all people, would ever contemplate involvement in shady dealings.

As for Herschelle Gibbs, he was one of South Africa's most prolific young players. According to the alleged transcripts, he had agreed to throw his wicket away cheaply, yet went on to make no less than 74 runs on the day. So that part of the story was clearly nonsense (a few months later we would learn that Gibbs had 'forgotten' about the deal).

Pieter Strydom? Surely not. Why would anyone in his right mind pay him to play badly? He had, after all, been doing that for free ever since he started playing for the Proteas! In an international career that spanned all of two tests and ten one-day internationals, Strydom had amassed a grand total of 83 runs and taken all of one wicket. Interestingly, he had made his debut in the now famous rain-plagued Centurion test against England in February 2000.

Finally, there were Henry Williams and Nicky Bojé. Once again, these two could hardly be described as superstars. Surely if you would want to make sure that you lose a match, you'd prefer players of top calibre to play along, not part-timers such as these two. Williams only ever played seven one-day international matches for South Africa.

Bojé had been in and out of the one-day squad since the tour to Zimbabwe in October 1995. However, until the start of the 2000 tour to India, he had participated in only 23 of the 111 one-day internationals that South Africa played over this period. His first test appearance came during the 2000 Indian tour. One could therefore say with confidence that Bojé would hardly be considered a key player at the time that the news of the match-fixing allegations first broke. Of course, to be fair, it must be added that he came into his own during the subsequent tour to Sri Lanka and Australia; in the latter he was actually chosen as Man of the One-Day Series.

So 'RUBBISH!' it clearly was. Dr Ali Bacher, Managing Director of the United Cricket Board of South Africa (UCBSA) soon released a statement in which he not only referred to Cronjé's 'unquestionable integrity and honesty' but expressed certainty that 'no South African cricketer has ever been involved in match-fixing'.

Because sport in this country has always been considered a matter of great national pride and importance, it was not long before the South African government became involved in the match-fixing debacle. Aziz Pahad, the Deputy Minister of Foreign Affairs, contacted the Indian government, seeking explanations regarding the investigation as well as the process by which the allegations had been made public. The Indian High Commissioner to South Africa was summoned to Pretoria in order to discuss the same issues, whilst The South African High Commissioner to India dropped in at the foreign ministry, requesting access to the tapes.

Relations between the two countries became strained. Accusations were flying in all directions. This was serious stuff – wars have been known to start for lesser reasons!

Cronjé himself entered the fray. 'I want to make it 100 percent clear that I deny ever receiving any sum of money during the one-day international series in India,' he said during a press conference held at Kingsmead in Durban, on Sunday the 9th of April 2000. 'I want to also make it absolutely clear that I have never spoken to any member of the team about throwing a game. We see 40 to 50 people going into our hotel rooms asking for individuals' autographs, interviews and pictures and to identify one or two individuals, as the allegations make out, would be very difficult.'

Stating that the allegations had hurt him and that the only way to clear his name would be for officials to speak to the players and check his bank accounts, Cronjé claimed that he had always believed match-fixing had no place in sport. 'In fact, I think sports betting has no place in sport.'

When 'Star News', India's premier news channel, aired the transcript, it made use of voice-overs to read the transcript as the original tapes had not been released by the police. Trevor Chesterfield, veteran South African cricket writer, was asked to comment after listening. As the voices were both of Asian origin (and Chesterfield had not been informed of the fact that he was listening to a re-enactment) the story soon spread that the tapes were fake. 'There are also serious doubts about the transcripts: the language, style of voice delivery and grammar are clumsy and the vernacular is decidedly non-South African in presentation,'

Chesterfield reported. 'RUBBISH!'

Support for Cronjé came from all sides. Graham Ford and Bob Woolmer, the current and former coaches of the South African national team respectively, dismissed the allegations. Pastor Ray McCauley, charismatic spiritual leader to the rich and famous, including Cronjé, added his not insignificant voice. Even Jaywant Lele, the secretary of the Indian Cricket Board, dismissed the allegations as – you've guessed it – 'rubbish'.

One of the few people not to reject the allegations out of hand, was national selector and former South African captain, Kepler Wessels. In the column which he writes for the *Saturday Star* he said that, '…this thing is rife in cricket and the biggest mistake we could make would be to try and sweep it under the carpet without an investigation'. Known to speak his mind, this comment was of particular significance, as Wessels had for many years been a mentor to Cronjé; they also shared a similar Afrikaner background. Rubbish? Four months later, Wessels would not be nominated to continue with his duties as a selector.

In the meantime, the Delhi-based businessman Rajesh Kalra was arrested. 'The series was fixed at 400,000 to 500,000 US dollars,' Kalra told the weekly magazine *India Today*. Rubbish?

On Monday the 10th of April 2000 I visited a kinesiologist in Johannesburg for treatment. As he treats some top sportsmen, I expressed interest in his opinion of the rumours. 'Oh, I'm sure it's true,' he said, quoting a television sports presenter and patient of his, who had apparently told him a long while before about corruption in cricket. Rubbish?

The following day the big news finally broke. Hansie Cronjé had sent a fax to the UCBSA in the early hours of the morning, admitting dishonesty and involvement with bookmakers. I was in a coffee shop in Sandton, waiting to interview a prospective new employee, when a colleague phoned me: the news had just been wired around the Reuters screens at our offices. I immediately phoned my mother to break it to her gently – she was, after all, Hansie's biggest fan.

I planned to fly back to Cape Town that afternoon. When I arrived at Johannesburg International Airport in order to catch my flight home, I joined a large group of people huddled around a television screen in the 'Lazy Leopard Watering Hole' pub. They were watching the UCBSA press conference in which Ali Bacher was providing details of Hansie's early-morning admission. Bacher announced that our South African cricket captain was now an ex-captain.

There was complete silence in the group of television watchers. We were absolutely stunned. Being at an airport, I couldn't help but think that news of a plane crash could hardly have created more shock than this.

Almost counter-intuitively, Hansie's confession led to a groundswell of support. When Cronjé himself organised a news conference later that same day, he was flanked by the Minister of Sport, Ngconde Balfour, who still referred to Hansie as 'my captain'.

South African newspapers promptly fuelled the fire. *The Star* published a poll two days after the confession to which more than 7 000 people responded, 94% of whom voted to allow Cronjé to play for his country again. The following weekend, the Afrikaans Sunday newspaper *Rapport* invited readers to submit faxes addressed to Hansie. A week later, *Rapport* stated that it had received thousands of messages all showing support for Cronjé, with only three or four expressing a contrary view. 'Young children write that he remains their hero, older women wish they had a son like Hansie and many others offer their condolences, knowing that he's already been forgiven by God,' the newspaper reported.

Much of the support for the sacked captain could possibly be attributed to the nature of his early confessions: an amount of less than 15,000 US dollars was mentioned by Cronjé; furthermore, he had insisted that he'd never actually thrown a match or even discussed the possibility of doing so with any of his team-mates.

Yet, a degree of scepticism grew concurrent to the support for Cronjé. Ironically, the reasons for this scepticism also related to the nature of Cronjé's confession. The question posed was why would he have risked his reputation and all his future earning power for so little? There must have been, so the sceptics thought, a great deal more money at stake than had been uncovered so far. Where there's smoke there's usually fire, and now that Cronjé had confirmed the existence of the smoke, many people began to suspect that there could in fact be a lot more fire.

Over the next two months many related developments took place around the world. The International Cricket Council (ICC) met in London, specifically to discuss match-fixing. A long-awaited report was published based on an investigation into alleged irregularities within Pakistani

15

cricket. Accusations, counter-accusations and denials were made. None of the test-cricket-playing countries were spared. Players were warned, fined and banned. The cricket world had been thrown into disarray.

And that was the good news. When the King Commission of Inquiry into match-fixing commenced at the beginning of June 2000, even more skeletons came out of the closet. Ali Bacher pointed fingers at other countries, implicating certain umpires in the process. Some of Hansie Cronjé's old team-mates seemed to turn against him, indicating that his heart-felt confession might have been less than frank. Cronjé himself revealed yet a third version of how events had occurred.

Two days later, I left a letter at Hansie Cronjé's Fancourt house, telling him that I wanted to write his book.

*   *   *   *   *

Something very interesting happened when I approached publishers with the concept of my book. Discussing it with the Managing Director of a niche publishing company which is involved in the field of sports publications, he made it quite clear to me that he wouldn't want to touch the book if there was any chance that it would bring sport – any sport – into disrepute. 'You've got to understand that sport is, after all, my business,' he said. In spite of this, he indicated an interest in the early drafts of the book and I left it with him for consideration. I never heard from the man again. Could this be construed as part of a cover-up to protect the vested interests of a range of stakeholders, I wondered? And if so, how long might this kind of thing have been going on?

Having said this, it should be understood that my intention has never been to be controversial or to bring the game of cricket into disrepute. The intention I have is simply to relay an objective account of the Hansie Cronjé saga. On the negative side, I could not help but include references to issues such as match-fixing and inappropriate betting – these discussions are after all being conducted in the public domain. On the positive side, I made a commitment to everyone I spoke to, most especially those close to Hansie Cronjé, that I would relay the good things they might have to say about him. I trust the text adequately reflects this.

In addition to this, I thought it interesting to analyse the issue from different angles and to draw various analogies. None of these could ever provide firm conclusions, but the exercise does throw up some interesting questions. For example: if we plot Hansie's form graphically over time, would any changes in trends be evident when comparing the periods before and after he started speaking to bookmakers (in terms of his own evidence)? How did these events compare with other instances of betting around the world, not only in cricket but also in other sports such as American baseball? These are just some of the issues covered in this book.

*   *   *   *   *

I still haven't heard from Hansie. But my conscience is clear: I didn't write this book behind his back. It was his choice not to co-operate.

*   *   *   *   *

> Writing is an adventure. To begin with, it is a toy and an amuse-
> ment. Then it becomes a mistress, then it becomes a master,
> then it becomes a tyrant. The last phase is that just as you are
> about to be reconciled to your servitude, you kill the monster
> and fling him to the public.
> (Winston Churchill)

1

The story unfolds

How did the Hansie Cronjé scandal ever happen? And why?

What role did his background and personality play in the build-up to the biggest shock in the history of South African sport? What can we learn from his captaincy and performance over the years? And how did things change after he started speaking to bookmakers? These are some of the issues of this book.

Before we can investigate the various aspects, however, it is necessary to provide a summary of the information contained in Cronjé's first confession, as well as the events as they transpired subsequent to that.

On 11 April 2000, Hansie Cronjé's early-morning fax, which was sent to Pastor Ray McCauley and the United Cricket Board of South Africa (UCBSA), stated that 'it' started after the fifth test against England, in January 2000. This test was played at Centurion, on the outskirts of Pretoria, and will be remembered for the fact that it rained for most of the match, before both teams forfeited an innings on the fifth and final day in order to make a match of it. England was set a target of 249 runs in 76 overs. They reached it with two wickets and five balls to spare, in one of the most exciting conclusions to a test match that South Africa had been involved in for some time.

The first name mentioned in Cronjé's confession was that of Hamid Cassim, somebody who had been 'hanging around the team for a few years now, always handing out biltong to the guys, in return for some tickets'. Cassim once told Cronjé that, if he had known that the captain was going to declare in that Centurion test, he could have made himself some good money. Cronjé replied, 'Why don't you ask?'

Hamid, or 'Banjo', as was his nickname, introduced Cronjé to a friend called Sanjay during the one-day international series involving England and Zimbabwe. According to Cronjé, the two of them told him that he could make some money if the team could 'maybe cook a match'. Cronjé's response was that he was not prepared to do this, unless the team was assured of a place in the final of the competition. Cronjé did, however, accept a cash amount of between $10,000 and $15,000 from Sanjay, just in case he had a change of mind.

According to Cronjé's confession, this was followed by further contact between himself, Cassim and Sanjay over the course of the one-day international series in India, during March 2000. Cronjé admitted that these discussions had centred around fixing matches, and that he had mentioned certain players' names in the process. Yet, he insisted that he had never actually spoken to any member of the South African team in this regard. Cronjé also mentioned that he did some forecasting with respect to some of the matches.

Apart from this, there were no other revelations in Cronjé's fax. He just made positive noises about his wife, his family, his friends, his team-mates, the South African cricket administrators and his religion. He even thanked the Indian police.

The start of a painful process

Two days after Hansie Cronjé's confession, the South African Minister of Sport initiated a judicial Commission of Inquiry into cricket match-fixing and related matters. Judge Edwin King, former Judge-President of the Cape, and a jurist with a strong human rights record, would later be appointed as Commissioner. Thus, the King Commission came into being.

The Terms of Reference of the King Commission were formulated in three parts:

- The first point had a narrow focus, and related only to the specific confession that Cronjé had made in respect of the cash amount he had accepted from a bookmaker (at the time of the one-day international series involving England and Zimbabwe, in January and

February 2000).

- The second point cast the net a bit wider, and covered a period of nearly six months, commencing with the start of the tour by the English team to South Africa in November 1999, and ending at the time that the South African leg of the one-day international series against Australia terminated (shortly after Cronjé made his confession in April 2000).
- The third point focused exclusively on an alleged match-fixing proposal to the South African cricket team, during its tour to India in 1996.

On Wednesday 7 June 2000, the King Commission finally convened at the Centre for the Book in Cape Town. An Edwardian design and a national monument, the building belongs to the South African Library and houses its manuscript collections. In a most predictable pun, the venue would, of course, soon be referred to as the Centre for the Bookie.

The first items of business on the agenda were separate applications by television station e.tv, and radio news provider Live Africa, to broadcast the hearings, on the premise that it was in the public interest to do so. The point was eloquently summed up by Paul Cainer, of Live Africa, when he said:

> These people are paid considerable salaries to play a game of cricket on a field to which the public is admitted by payment. The public has the right to know whether the money that they have been paying to go and watch these people play and earn large salaries, has been earned by fair competition or by some pre-arrangement ...

The point was immediately opposed by the lawyers of most of the parties, based on the fact that it would place undesirable strain on the participants in the proceedings. Twenty-four hours later, Judge King exercised his discretion and ruled that broadcasting would not be allowed. The matter was, however, taken to the High Court, where the decision was overturned within two weeks. From Wednesday 21 June onwards (which was only the seventh day of the Commission's hearings, coinciding with the start of Hansie Cronjé's cross-examination), all evidence before the King Commission was therefore televised in full.

Back to Day 1 of the King Commission. At last, it was time to call on the first witness. Neill Andrews, a well-known television presenter and wagering expert, enlightened the Commission with his considerable knowledge of the world of betting. A key point was that the concept of spread-betting could be applied to nearly anything. Andrews illustrated this with the THUD spread, once offered by bookmakers Ladbrokes in the United Kingdom, which related to the remaining hours that Emperor Tito would lie on his deathbed (THUD standing for Tito's Hours Until Death).

The next witness was Pat Symcox, the first in a batting line-up of exactly eleven players and ex-players who would eventually appear before the Commission, in addition to Hansie Cronjé himself. Symcox, an off-spinner with a test century to his name, first played international cricket at the ripe old age of 33, and has always been known for his fighting spirit and his straight talking.

Symmo, as he is popularly known, was the first player to provide a rather detailed account to the Commission about an incident which had, over time, become fairly well known in South African cricket circles. This was the offer extended to the South African cricket team to lose (or 'throw') a match during their tour to India at the end of 1996; the specific issue of the third point in the Commission's terms of reference.

The incident took place at the end of a two-month tour, during which the South Africans played three tests (losing the series 2-1) as well as seven one-day internationals. The last match was a limited-overs affair in Mumbai, which had originally been planned as a benefit match only for one of the Indian players, but was eventually upgraded to have full international status. A number of the South African players were sick at the end of a difficult tour; most of them were unhappy that the match had been upgraded and hardly anyone was in the mood to play.

Over the course of the hearings, there would be fairly general agreement amongst the players regarding the salient features of how this incident transpired. Hansie Cronjé took an offer to the team to lose the match in return for a total amount of between $200,000 and $250,000 (the players' recollections differ on the exact amount). The offer was discussed and rejected, with strongest resistance coming from Andrew

Hudson, Derek Crookes and Daryll Cullinan. After the decision had been made and the meeting had ended, some of the players, including Symcox, Brian McMillan, Fanie de Villiers and Dave Richardson, stayed behind with Cronjé. In a 'joke', according to the players' evidence, Cronjé phoned the person who had made the offer and first negotiated an additional $100,000 before rejecting it.

The offer was clearly considered seriously. As Pat Symcox said in his evidence, $250,000 is 'quite a lot of money, you know, especially when you divide it by the Rand'. It's even more when you multiply it ...

The Pat Symcox, tongue-in-cheek brand of humour was demonstrated on a number of different occasions over the course of his testimony. When advocate Shamila Batohi, leader of the evidence for the King Commission, asked him where he thought the offer to throw the match in Mumbai had come from, he said, '... you would assume it wouldn't be from the Prime Minister ...'

Symcox also told the Commission about two other occasions during which he had been approached in the context of match-fixing. The first one was not dwelled on, but it concerned an international player (not South African), who had approached Symcox in India.

But the second one did relate to a South African player ... a player called Hansie Cronjé. According to Symmo, the newly appointed captain approached him at the time of the Mandela Trophy match against Pakistan, in Cape Town. Cronjé wanted to discuss an offer to throw the match, but Symcox rejected the idea. As it turned out, South Africa won the match quite comfortably.

Although there was no doubt in Symcox's mind about the specific match in question, he got the date slightly wrong, thinking that it had happened in 1997. But the match did, in fact, take place in January 1995, nearly two years *before* the offer that was put to the whole team in Mumbai.

What was interesting, was that the Mandela Trophy incident fell outside the specific terms of reference of the King Commission. From an objective point of view there can be no doubt that this was relevant information, yet at the start of Symcox's testimony there was a lot of debate over the admissibility of the evidence. Notably, the disclosures were vociferously opposed by Hansie Cronjé's legal counsel.

* * * * *

23

The story unfolds

Day 2 of the King Commission opened with the testimony of Derek Crookes. Similar to his colleague Symcox before him, Crookes was an off-break bowler and a fine batsman, and he'd been in and out of the South African side since the 1994/1995 season. He captained South African Schools in 1988, the year following Hansie Cronjé.

Crookes elaborated on the 1996 offer in Mumbai and pointed out that he was first approached on the plane on the way there (before the full team meeting). It was his impression that the other members of the team had also been approached individually, in addition to the eventual meeting. Crookes further recalled that Hansie Cronjé had said that nobody should know about the issue, not even the players' wives. He did, however, also point out that the imperative to keep things secret disappeared later on, and that the issue actually became a bit of a joke amongst the players.

The evidence turned to the 2000 tour of India. Firstly, Crookes said that after the first match he was specifically informed that he would not open the bowling for the rest of the tour. In the fifth and final one-day international, played in Nagpur, he did, however, open the bowling (an issue that would later be questioned). Furthermore, in that same match in Nagpur, Crookes testified that he was surprised at not being replaced as a bowler after a spell of five overs, during which he had been 'taken to the cleaners' by the Indian batsmen.

During the cross-examination of Derek Crookes, the first of many legal wrangles over one specific point was witnessed. The admissibility of references to the transcripts of the alleged telephone conversations between Hansie Cronjé and a bookmaker, widely reported in the press, would end up being a thorny issue throughout the King Commission's proceedings. The original tapes would obviously be vital evidence, yet the Indian authorities would not make them available.

Most of the lawyers present, including those of Derek Crookes, did not have a problem with references to the transcripts, but Hansie Cronjé's legal counsel raised objections. Judge King eventually gave a provisional ruling, allowing the references.

Next in line was Daryll Cullinan. One of his country's most prolific batsmen of all time, having scored more test centuries than any other South African at the time of writing this book (not to mention the numerous

24

other records held by him), Cullinan was also one of the more senior players remaining in the Protea squad at the time of the hearings.

Like Derek Crookes, Cullinan was one of the players who could claim the moral high ground after rejecting the Mumbai offer in 1996, more strongly than most of the other members of the squad. In Cullinan's testimony, however, he put forward a view that the offer had perhaps not been serious, and that Hansie Cronjé merely used it to test the moral fibre of the team. He also thought it might simply have been a ploy by the captain to motivate the team, as they were at an emotional low at the end of a tough tour.

There was further reference to his views at the time of the declaration in the test match against England at Centurion, when both sides forfeited an innings. At first, Cullinan opposed the decision on the basis that England had been given too many overs to score the required runs. When the eighth English wicket fell, however, he walked over to Hansie Cronjé and told him that the two of them could have a beer together afterwards.

After Daryll Cullinan, it was the turn of Rory Steyn to testify. Steyn, once the chief bodyguard to President Nelson Mandela, was a security consultant to the UCBSA and was staying in the same hotel as the South African team on 10 and 11 April 2000. Steyn was called to Cronjé's room at two o'clock in the morning on 11 April, and was therefore the first person to become aware of the dramatic turn of events that was about to unfold.

Rory Steyn relayed his account of how matters transpired on the morning of 11 April. According to him, the South African captain was on the verge of tears when he got to his room, saying that the lies could not go on any longer. He told Steyn that the conversations that had been reported in the press were true, but promptly went on to say that he'd never actually spoken to any other player about accepting money ...

Cronjé then handed Steyn the handwritten statement which would later be faxed to Pastor Ray McCauley and others. In Steyn's presence, however, Cronjé first changed the amount of cash he'd received from an original $20,000 or $25,000 to the final version of between $10,000 and $15,000.

According to Steyn's testimony, Hansie Cronjé said to him that he didn't want to make any contact with the players. Hansie did, however, pass on a message to Herschelle Gibbs via Steyn, saying, 'Herschelle, don't worry, you're not involved. The captain says you've got nothing to worry about. Stay strong and get your mind on the game.'

It was the very same Herschelle Gibbs who testified next. Probably the most gifted and versatile sportsman in the Protea squad, Gibbs once represented South African Schools not only in cricket, but also in rugby and soccer.

It had been a stressful couple of months for Herschelle Gibbs. His name had been mentioned in the alleged transcripts of phone conversations in India and, based on that, he was questioned on a continuous basis about his possible involvement in matters of match-fixing. After originally pleading total ignorance, Gibbs eventually admitted to Dr Ali Bacher, over the telephone on 19 April 2000, that he had been approached by Hansie Cronjé. He insisted, however, that he'd turned down the offer. It later transpired that, in all these responses, Herschelle was essentially still following instructions given to him by Hansie Cronjé. Furthermore, he was trying to protect not only himself, but also his ex-captain.

So, when 8 June 2000 eventually arrived, there was finally an opportunity for Herschelle Gibbs to 'come clean' and reveal, on a legal platform, all the details of what had actually happened.

In spite of all the nervous tension, there was, thankfully, a light moment at the start of Gibbs's testimony. Advocate to the players, Mike Fitzgerald, mistakenly put it to Gibbs that he was first selected to play for his country in 1999. When Gibbs pointed out that the correct year was, in fact, 1996, Fitzgerald said, 'That was just to test you.' In a flash, Gibbs responded by saying, 'I passed that one.'

Herschelle Gibbs was present at the 1996 team meeting in Mumbai, where the offer to throw a match was discussed, but he was a very junior member of the squad at the time and he hardly participated in the discussion. As a consequence, that incident formed a minor part of his cross-examination before the King Commission.

But, unfortunately, there was no such luck with the final match of the 2000 Indian tour. The game was played in Nagpur on 19 March, coincidentally the same date as Herschelle's mother's birthday. Gibbs testified how Hansie Cronjé had come into the room, shared by

26

Herschelle and Henry Williams, with a huge grin on his face. The captain offered both of them $15,000 to play badly: Gibbs had to score less than 20 runs, and Williams had to concede more than 50 runs in his 10 overs of bowling.

Both of the players promptly agreed, asking Cronjé, as an afterthought, to try and get more than the $15,000 that had been promised. However, once the innings started, Gibbs (in his own words) 'batted like a steam train', hit fours off the first two balls he faced and went on to score 74 runs off 53 balls. Predictably, he never got the $15,000.

The significance of this evidence can hardly be emphasised enough. The earlier disclosure by Pat Symcox, relating to Cronjé's approach to him in 1995, can perhaps be discarded as not so material, or such 'old news' that it no longer really mattered. But this was fresh, hard information, within the terms of reference of the King Commission. And it was certainly not a joke that could simply be discarded. Moreover, it indicated, once and for all, that Hansie Cronjé's 11 April confession fell short of the truth.

It was the vice-captain of the Proteas, Mark Boucher, who eventually convinced Herschelle Gibbs to tell the full story to the King Commission. Boucher invited Gibbs for a drink on 31 May 2000, a week before the Commission began, and pointed out that he could go to jail if he lied in court (at that stage, Gibbs had only admitted to receiving an offer, not accepting one). In a memorable twist of irony, it had been the same Mark Boucher who ran Gibbs out, with his score on 74, on that fateful day in Nagpur.

In his evidence, Herschelle Gibbs repeatedly called Hansie Cronjé a friend and a mentor. He also spoke about his utmost respect for the man. It was clear that Cronjé had tremendous influence over Gibbs. No doubt this played a crucial role in Herschelle's agreement, in a moment of weakness and stupidity, to play along with the captain's plan. Within twenty-four hours of Herschelle Gibbs's testimony before the King Commission, the UCBSA suspended him and withdrew him from the touring squad that would commence with a tour to Sri Lanka three weeks later. Gibbs would eventually be the only player in this position: no-one else who finally admitted to any wrongdoing before the King Commission was in the Protea squad at that stage.

* * * * *

Day 3 of the King Commission started with the incessant ringing of an alarm. When Mike Fitzgerald suggested an adjournment so that the sound could be identified, Judge King responded with one of his many witticisms by saying, 'Well, I think the sound has been identified; it's an alarm. It's a question of finding a button to switch it off, presumably.'

Soon after, it was time for the testimony of Henry Williams. Due to the fact that his room-mate in Nagpur, Herschelle Gibbs, had taken the stand less than twenty-four hours before him and proceeded to provide a much fuller account of events than had been heard before, there was not much left for the fast-medium-pace bowler from Boland to reveal to the Commission.

Like Gibbs, Williams did not follow through in terms of the match-fixing arrangement with Hansie Cronjé, although the circumstances in his case happened to be quite different. He opened the bowling for South Africa that day (the first time in his career that he ever did that) and promptly took the prize wicket of Ganguly in his second over. He did not bowl another ball, however, leaving the field with a shoulder strain that had been bothering him since the first match of the series ten days earlier. Like Herschelle Gibbs, Henry Williams never saw the $15,000.

Describing the problem that he had with his shoulder to the King Commission, Henry Williams used the Latin biological term for the injury. When the interpreter battled with the translation (Williams was giving his testimony in Afrikaans), Judge King asked – to tremendous laughter – 'Is there a Roman in the house?'

In the weeks and months leading up to the start of the King Commission, Henry Williams had denied involvement in matters of a match-fixing nature, in much the same way as Herschelle Gibbs. According to his evidence before the Commission, Williams was never contacted by Hansie Cronjé over this period. The ex-captain did, however, send him a number of messages through Gibbs, instructing Williams to pass the whole incident off as a joke.

Clearly, the relationship between Williams and Cronjé was nowhere near as strong as that between Gibbs and the ex-captain. To a certain extent this is understandable, given that Hansie Cronjé and Herschelle

Gibbs had shared so much more over the years. Henry Williams had, after all, only ever played seven one-day international matches for South Africa. Having said this, however, it does not seem fair for Cronjé to ignore Williams in the way that he appeared to have done after the scandal broke, given that Cronjé was instrumental in the trouble in which Williams ended up finding himself. In this regard there is one response by Williams, to a question posed by Mike Fitzgerald, that stands out above all. '… I also agreed because I had a lot of respect for the captain, Hansie Cronjé. If he can do something like this, why couldn't I do it?…'

It was the turn of Pieter Strydom to testify next. An atmosphere of nervous anticipation filled the Centre for the Book as he took the stand. After all, here was another player whose name had been mentioned in the transcripts. Would Strydom, like Gibbs and Williams before him, also come up with some 'fresh' revelations?

Indeed he would. Not once, but twice.

Firstly, Strydom told the Commission that Hansie Cronjé was interested in what the odds might be for South Africa to win the Centurion test, after the much-publicised declaration and innings forfeiture. Strydom, who was playing in his first test, proceeded to phone a friend, asking him to place two R50 bets; one for himself, and one on behalf of the South African captain. The bets were, however, never actually placed. There were no odds available.

OK, so a R50 bet doesn't sound like such a big deal. But, in terms of the regulations pertaining to players' conduct, it is. And worse was to follow.

A month later, South Africa played in the first test on their tour to India. The venue? Mumbai. Again.

Pieter Strydom told the King Commission that he was approached by Hansie Cronjé the night before the test started, and offered R70,000 if the team scored less than 250 (the offer would later be doubled, 'jokingly', to R140,000). According to Strydom he turned it down, but he did say that he might have considered it, had he already played 80 or 90 tests at that stage. Self-incriminating, perhaps, but honest.

'As your first test was at the age of 30, that would have taken you to possibly the most ancient cricketer of all times,' the Commissioner remarked.

'Especially at the rate I'm playing test matches; one a year,' was Pieter Strydom's self-effacing response.

The Mumbai test was the second and last test match in which Pieter Strydom would ever play (unless he gets another belated recall to the Protea squad – not something considered to be likely). Two tests ... and two stories to tell about betting and bookmakers. This is one 100% record that may stand for some time.

As was the case with the incident in Nagpur, as disclosed by Herschelle Gibbs and Henry Williams, Strydom's account of events in Mumbai was hard, new, and damning evidence against Hansie Cronjé, who had said in his 11 April confession that he never spoke to other players. The audience could hardly wait to hear Cronjé's response.

There was one other point in Pieter Strydom's testimony that was interesting. While being cross-examined by Shamila Batohi, Strydom discussed a telephonic conversation between himself and Hansie Cronjé that took place after the scandal broke. Having mentioned the fact that Cronjé had told him 'the furore was about one-day internationals and had nothing to do with the tests', Strydom went on to say, 'No, because he just said that the one-dayers. They were mentioning the one-dayers, they were talking about the one-dayers; the third and fifth one-dayers, in India, and I wasn't involved, and I was never approached for those one-dayers. And he said it had nothing to do with the first test. That's when he approached me; for the first test.'

The significant aspect of this response was the reference to the third one-day international in India. Bear in mind that news was out already about the fifth one, in which the Gibbs/Williams incident took place. But Shamila Batohi did not follow up by asking Pieter Strydom why he mentioned this third match.

What happened in the third one-day international, played in Faridabad? The score card shows that India batted first and scored 248 runs in their allotted 50 overs; South Africa knocked it off with two wickets and two overs to spare.

When looking at the individual performances in that game, it is noteworthy that Hansie Cronjé was chosen as Man of the Match. But he probably did not get the accolade for his bowling: Cronjé brought himself on as first change bowler and sent down a full complement of 10 overs, ending with figures of 1/69. The other three bowlers who bowled 10 overs each (Shaun Pollock, Steve Elworthy and Jacques Kallis), conceded 36, 44 and 37 runs respectively. The 'fifth bowler' was a combined effort by four players, namely, Lance Klusener (who wasn't particularly expensive in the two overs he bowled, ending with figures of 0/11), Nicky Bojé (0/22 in four overs), Dale Benkenstein (0/9 in one over) and Pieter Strydom (0/15 in three overs). In combination, their figures added up to 0/57 in 10 overs, with Benkenstein being the only expensive one.

On the batting front, Gary Kirsten top-scored for South Africa with 93 runs from 111 balls; Hansie Cronjé made 66 from 71 balls. Of all the South African batsmen who achieved double figures on the day, Herschelle Gibbs, with 19 runs from 29 balls, had the lowest strike rate.

One wonders why Hansie Cronjé even won the Man of the Match award that day. He scored less runs than Gary Kirsten, he didn't score much faster than Gary Kirsten, and he didn't take a catch or effect a run-out. One can also not say that it was because Cronjé played a more important innings than Kirsten, as the two of them shared the match-winning fourth-wicket partnership of 113 runs in 20 overs. And with the exception of two other bowlers (one Indian and one South African) who, between them, bowled a total of only three overs in the match, Cronjé's bowling figures were worse than anyone else's on the day. Interestingly, Hansie Cronjé would testify some two weeks after Pieter Strydom, and tell the Commission how he told Mark Boucher on the morning of that match that he had a good feeling … and that he was going to win the Man of the Match award.

But to get back to the real question. Why did Pieter Strydom ever mention this specific match? And why did Shamila Batohi not probe him on it?

After Pieter Strydom it was the turn of Nicky Bojé to take the stand. Like Hansie Cronjé, Nicky Bojé was an Afrikaner from Bloemfontein. Like Hansie Cronjé, Nicky Bojé was schooled at Grey College (Bojé was in standard six when Cronjé matriculated). Like Hansie Cronjé, Nicky Bojé had been a captain of the South African Schools side. And like Hansie Cronjé, Nicky Bojé had been implicated in the Indian phone transcripts.

Understandably, there was, once again, a great deal of anticipation in the air when Bojé took the oath. But from the point of view of the sensation seekers, Bojé's testimony ended up being a rank anticlimax.

Nicky Bojé confirmed that he and Hansie Cronjé had been close friends for a long time. ('Since Mr. Bojé's birth ...' Cronjé himself would later testify.) Yes, he was shocked and disappointed about news of the scandal. Yes, they'd spoken to each other since. But no, he was never approached by Hansie. Never. He even offered to take a lie detector test in this regard.

So why did his name feature in the transcripts? 'I've got no idea,' Bojé said. '... I think the only person that can say anything about it, is Hansie himself.'

Fair enough, it would appear.

Bronwyn Anne Wilkinson-Luck, recently appointed Communications Manager of the UCBSA, and ex-crime reporter at *The Star* newspaper, was next.

Wilkinson explained her role as news of the scandal broke. She was the first person to inform Hansie Cronjé, telephonically, about the rumours on 7 April 2000. She got 'kind of a snort laugh' from Cronjé in response. After listening to Hansie Cronjé's denials, it was Wilkinson who drew up the media release on behalf of the UCBSA, in which Cronjé was quoted as saying, 'The allegations are completely without substance ...'

Wilkinson also testified that she had known about 'the '96 thing', as she called it: the original Mumbai offer. She remembered reading about that in the press a year or more previously. Interestingly, her memory in this regard appeared to be better than that of Dr Ali Bacher, who would testify the following day.

Wilkinson was the first witness to introduce the name of one Marlon Aronstam to the Commission. She was informed by *The Star* newspaper that they had been tipped off to look into his affairs. Aronstam's name would only feature again when Cronjé took the stand a few days later.

There was also a discussion about Hamid Cassim, as well as the speculation that it had been Lance Klusener who blew the whistle on Hansie Cronjé. (Klusener denied this.) Apart from that, there wasn't much else to report.

The Commission adjourned for the weekend.

On Sunday, 11 June, the dramatic news broke that Hansie Cronjé had been offered indemnity from prosecution by the National Director of

Public Prosecutions, Bulelani Ngcuka.

The deal was struck after an approach by Cronjé's lawyers and discussions between Ngcuka, Minister of Justice, Penuell Maduna, Minister of Sport, Ngconde Balfour and the King Commission's chief investigator, Shamila Batohi. The indemnity was conditional upon the King Commission finding that he made a full disclosure, and that he was honest and truthful in every respect. The arrangement would also apply to Herschelle Gibbs and Henry Williams.

An offer of indemnity to someone, the extent of whose guilt was as yet undetermined, seemed like an overly generous gesture in the eyes of many. On the other hand, the benefit of the arrangement was that it was likely to facilitate a fuller disclosure of the truth by an individual who might otherwise respond to questions in an evasive fashion, on the basis that truthful answers could be self-incriminatory.

*　*　*　*　*

And so to Monday, 12 June 2000: Day 4 of the King Commission's hearings.

The day opened with a short appearance by a Reserve Bank official who provided details of two cash deposits, totalling an amount of $47,630, which had been made on Hansie Cronjé's behalf.

After this came the turn to testify of the Managing Director of the UCBSA (and one of a small number of people able to pronounce the word 'cricket' so that it sounds as if it consists of only one syllable), Dr Ali Bacher. Not someone with a reputation for being particularly publicity-shy, Dr Bacher volunteered that his testimony be carried live on national television.

Ali Bacher is a medical doctor by profession, who captained Transvaal at the tender age of 21. He went on to captain the South African national team in their whitewash of the Australian touring team in 1970. One could, therefore, say with some safety that he knows a bit about the game.

Bacher told the Commission how well the Board looked after its players. He spoke of the high regard that he had for Hansie Cronjé, calling him 'a serious man, a deep thinker, a very committed person, a good family man and very good, honest South African'. He also spoke of his support for the captain, even after the first news broke. He then told the Commission how it took him and Percy Sonn two to three minutes to decide that Hansie Cronjé should be withdrawn from the South African team, after Cronjé's early-morning confession over the telephone on 11 April 2000.

The first really significant point in Bacher's testimony, however, was when he spoke about a conversation that he and Jonty Rhodes had had, following a meeting with the team, later that same day. Rhodes spoke to him about the 1996 offer in Mumbai. Bacher claimed that this was the first time he ever heard of the incident, except for a short discussion ('... for about 5, 10 seconds, out of nowhere ...') with Hansie Cronjé, which took place 'about a few weeks before these revelations emerged in South Africa'.

Bacher could not recall ever reading a report in this regard, by Colin Bryden, published in *The Sunday Times* in 1998, entitled 'Proud South African Cricketers Hit Match-Fixers for Six'. According to Bacher's testimony, the reason for this was as follows: 'I might have been overseas, I might have not got that newspaper ...'

This is interesting, as one would expect somebody who is in charge of any big business (as cricket is), to be aware of or, indeed, to be made aware of, any publicity which goes to the core of such a business. One would further expect that same manager to remember such publicity a few years later.

The Sunday Times has been South Africa's most widely read newspaper for many years. According to the official statistics produced by the Audit Bureau of Circulations, this newspaper sold an average of 449,000 copies per week during the second half of 1998 – nearly 25% more than the Afrikaans newspaper, *Rapport*, in second place.

The Sunday Times article, dated 20 December 1998, was published at a time when corruption in cricket was very much in the news. The ICC had brought out a media release only eleven days earlier, announcing that Mark Waugh and Shane Warne had been disciplined in 1995, for providing information to a bookmaker. A few days later, the ICC brought out a follow-up media release.

On 14 December 1998, the President of the ICC and close associate of Dr Ali Bacher, Mr Jagmohan Dalmiya, said that the 'ICC shall collect *all possible available data* and discuss the matter thoroughly' (author's emphasis), during forthcoming meetings in January 1999. Mr Dalmiya said further, that the ICC might set up 'a high powered Commission to investigate and inquire into the issue'.

And what did the article in *The Sunday Times* say? That Hansie Cronjé had informed the reporter about the offer in Mumbai, and that it was raised at a team meeting – where it was basically laughed off. The article also discussed some dubious incidents from the Mandela Trophy series. 'The sooner it is sorted out, the better,' Cronjé was quoted as saying. In the same article, Dr Ali Bacher himself was quoted, in response to the ICC announcement which had been made six days earlier. Bacher expressed confidence in the integrity of his own players and commented that, over the years, the issue had not enjoyed 'the attention it deserves' at the ICC level.

Judge King asked Dr Bacher specifically whether he recalled ex-Protea coach, Bob Woolmer, telling him about the 1996 incident. Bacher denied ever having any such recollection. The judge then asked Bacher whether he would have taken the matter further if Woolmer had, in fact, informed him thereof. Ali Bacher replied, 'Absolutely.'

In his testimony, Bacher continually focused on the official tour reports, prepared by the coach and the manager after completion of the 1996 tour to India, in which there was evidently no official mention of the offer.

However, it was reported in the press that Bob Woolmer insisted he had mentioned the incident in despatches to Dr Ali Bacher and in meetings with the UCBSA. 'I am not going to get into whether he remembers or not, because I know that he has a lot on his plate,' Woolmer was quoted as saying.

Ali Bacher also told the Commission about an acquaintance of his, an Indian bookmaker with impeccable credentials, identified only as 'Mr. R', from whom he had learnt a thing or two about match-fixing in the cricket world. Bacher did not hesitate to mention details of incidents or names of people that were allegedly 'on the payroll', including that of umpire Javed Akhtar from Pakistan. In the fifth test between South Africa and England at Headingley, in August 1999, eight LBW decisions were given against South Africa: seven of them dubious decisions by Akhtar, according to Bacher.

A most entertaining letter was then read out to the Commission. It was a letter written to Ali Bacher by Jacques Sellschop, Group Executive of

Corporate Relations at MTN, a large cellular network company in South Africa and an important sponsor of cricket in the country. According to Sellschop, he sat next to Shoaib Akhtar, the Pakistani fast bowler, or his 'genetic double', on a flight between Johannesburg and Durban on 18 April 2000. The bowler was supposedly in South Africa for some medical treatment.

The two of them struck up a conversation and Sellschop was given numerous 'insights' into match-fixing, the Pakistani way. Without a doubt, the best sentence in the Sellschop letter was the following: 'The enjoyment of the spectators is not compromised, because they do not know what outcome has been arranged and therefore the suspense element is not diluted.'

It remains unclear to this day who the person sitting next to Mr. Sellschop actually was. According to the Pakistan cricket authorities, Akhtar was in the squad touring the West Indies at the time. But, according to the records, he was not playing in any match over the period of the alleged incident.

Getting back to Hansie Cronjé himself, there is, perhaps, no better way to close off this section, than to quote Dr Bacher, when he said the following to the King Commission: 'I would sum up my feelings as follows, that if the bookmakers can get to Hansie Cronjé, they can get to anybody in world cricket.'

After Dr Ali Bacher's testimony, which had taken up the entire morning and some of the afternoon of the fourth day of the King Commission, it was time for Lance Klusener to enter the fray. The most exciting addition to the game of cricket since the advent of the one-day game itself, Klusener batted and bowled himself into the record books in double-quick time, culminating in the Man of the Tournament award at the 1999 World Cup.

When he took the stand, some general background questions were put to the Zulu-speaking all-rounder. In particular, he was asked to confirm that he was a left-handed batsman. 'I'm glad you've got it right,' he responded, evoking much laughter throughout the room.

In the next question he was asked to confirm that he was, indeed, an all-rounder. 'I'm getting there,' he said. 'Hurriedly, I think,' the Commissioner added.

Time for the serious business. When Lance Klusener walks to the wicket, he does not have a reputation for beating about the bush. This day would not be different.

Within minutes, Zulu was at it again. Klusener told the Commission how Hansie Cronjé came into a room before the second test of the Indian tour, in March 2000. The captain asked Klusener, Jacques Kallis and Mark Boucher whether they were interested in an offer of sorts. They declined; the discussion lasted only a few seconds, and Cronjé left.

At first, the three of them didn't really think Cronjé was serious. It was only much later on, after the news had broken of the alleged phone transcripts, that they reconsidered …

Mark Boucher, newly appointed vice-captain of the South African cricket team, padded up next. Holder of the unofficial record for the highest score by a night watchman, he would also take the stand last on this day at the King Commission.

Having been subject to the same approach by Hansie Cronjé as the one described by Lance Klusener to the Commission only a little while earlier, Boucher didn't have much information to add.

He could only enlighten the meeting with regard to the circumstances when the approach took place. Boucher, Klusener and Kallis were having pasta; they'd made far too much and asked other players to join in. As the Commissioner remarked, 'there wasn't a team dog at that stage…'.

* * * * *

When the King Commission resumed on Tuesday 13 June 2000 for its fifth day of hearings, Dr Ali Bacher took the stand for another brief appearance.

The purpose, this time, was to clear up confusion from the previous afternoon about a statement ascribed to Robbie Muzzell, team manager during the 1996 tour to India, and an Executive Committee member of the UCBSA, about when he learnt of the offer that was discussed by the team at the end of that tour.

The bottom line, according to the testimony during this follow-up appearance by Bacher, was that Muzzell indicated he only learnt about the full details of that offer on 14 April 2000.

Then it was the turn of Jacques Kallis, the last of the pasta brigade. Kallis did not have much to add to the details of the incident, as described by Lance Klusener and Mark Boucher before him. A lot of his cross-examination centred around South Africa's innings forfeiture in the Centurion test. He made it quite clear how much he opposed the decision, as he believed that the target set for England was too easy. As Kallis said, '… I know how difficult it is to win a test match, and you don't give stuff like that away …'

But Hansie Cronjé was adamant; 'He wanted to make a game of it, rather than having a boring day's cricket,' Kallis said.

Next up was Dave Richardson. The previous wicketkeeper of the Proteas, and an attorney by profession, Richardson currently acts as the Commercial Representative of the South African cricket team.

At the beginning of Richardson's testimony he relayed an anecdote which he had been using successfully at after-dinner speeches for some time. Asked why his batting average in one-day internationals was so low, he said the reason was that 'people like Kallis and them batted, for the majority of the overs, very slowly, and then the captain used to normally say, "You know, go out there, we need 20 an over. Don't take any chances"'.

The same after-dinner speeches that Richardson so often makes soon featured on a much more serious note, however. In his statement to the Commission, Richardson said that he sometimes referred to the team discussion about the 1996 Mumbai offer in these speeches; the point being that it wasn't really considered to be a secret. Quite rightly, Shamila Batohi proceeded to ask him whether he found it strange, therefore, 'that no member of the UCB Management became aware of this offer until very recently'.

Richardson's answer was not convincing. 'Not particularly,' he said, '… you know, you don't reach that many people with your after-dinner speeches. And there are many people in this room, probably, who would never have known about it …'

But then, one dares say, most of the people in that room, that day, were probably not involved in running a business called South African cricket. And most people will agree that word does tend to get around, especially when it concerns something 'juicy'.

Not much else of significance emanated from Dave Richardson's testimony. The day ended early; the hearings would only reconvene two days later.

Hansie Cronjé, the ex-captain himself, would be next in the witness box.

When one cuts through all the evidence over the first five days of the King Commission's hearings, a clear picture emerges. Day by day, and slice by slice, more and more of the truth salami was offered to the Commission.

Prior to the Commission, Hansie Cronjé himself had only volunteered the first – and rather thin – slice by confessing on 11 April 2000 that he'd taken an amount of between $10,000 and $15,000 from a bookmaker. This was said to be in return for potentially changing his mind about wanting to fix matches, and approaching other players in that regard – which Cronjé had previously said he never did.

There was, of course, that other slice of salami which, by now, was a bit stale, as it had been in the public domain for some time. Many people, with the notable exception of Dr Ali Bacher, did, after all, know about the team discussion around the Mumbai offer in 1996.

The third slice was the Pat Symcox disclosure, relating to Cronjé approaching him, in the context of a match-fixing offer, at the time of the Mandela Trophy in January 1995.

Slice number four would lead to much indigestion: it concerned two players who were not only approached by Hansie Cronjé, but who actually agreed to play along and underperform in a match in India. Herschelle Gibbs and Henry Williams would have to live with the consequences of their actions for evermore.

Slice number five was perhaps slightly less filling, yet equally unpalatable. Pieter Strydom revealed the approach that was made to him, also in India. Thankfully, he declined. Oh yes, there was another morsel – a R50 bet that should never have been …

And slice number six was the approach to Lance Klusener, Mark Boucher and Jacques Kallis – in India once more. This one happened over a bowl of pasta, an appropriately Italian dinner setting, to conclude the initial offering of a salami called truth.

Now, at last, it was Hansie Cronjé's turn to testify. And everybody wondered: how much more salami?

Thursday, 15 June, finally arrived: Day 6 of the King Commission. The hors d'oeuvres were finished. Bring on the main course.

The hall was crowded to capacity. The television cameras were there; Hansie Cronjé had agreed to go live before the nation. A day later, it would be announced that, in any event, broadcasting rights had been granted. The cameras became a fixture.

Before Cronjé started to read out his statement, Judge Edwin King reminded him that he should volunteer all information. The judge also quoted Chapter 8 from St John's Gospel to Cronjé: 'The truth will set you free.'

The much-awaited Hansie Cronjé statement followed. Slice by slice, and in chronological order, Cronjé dealt with the slices of salami as had been revealed by the players who had testified before him.

Mandela Trophy approach, January 1995, à la Symcox. Check. Cronjé testified how he had been approached by 'an Indian or Pakistani man, who described himself only as 'John'. An amount of 'about $10,000' was offered for the South African team to throw the game. The offer was discussed with Pat Symcox, but not accepted.

First test in Mumbai, February 2000, à la Strydom. Check. Before telling us more about this offer, Cronjé elaborated on his relationship with Hamid Cassim and Sanjay, the two gentlemen whose names he'd volunteered in his 13 April confession. In short, having taken money from Sanjay, Cronjé found that he 'had got into something from which it was very difficult to get out'. Cronjé also accepted a mobile phone from Sanjay in India; this would be used to phone the captain on a regular basis, applying pressure to fix matches.

Second test in Bangalore, March 2000, à la Klusener, Boucher and Kallis. Check. Again, Cronjé blamed the pressure as applied by Sanjay. After this, Cronjé said that he pretended to play along in terms of an arrangement to lose the first one-day international in Cochin, but he did nothing about it. South Africa did, in fact, lose the match, but they scored too many runs. Cronjé got no money. For the next three one-day internationals he only did some forecasting – free of charge.

Fifth one-day international in Nagpur, 2000, à la Gibbs and Williams. Check. The pressure from Sanjay had built up even more and

Cronjé gave in. But Herschelle Gibbs played a gem of an innings and Cronjé, himself, scored a quick 38 runs. South Africa posted their highest one-day score against India and won the match. And that spelt the end of the contact with Sanjay.

What else was in Hansie Cronjé's statement to the King Commission?

Firstly, Cronjé told the Commission about 'someone known to me as Sunil' who approached him in the context of possible match-fixing, on the 1996 tour of India. But Cronjé said he declined this offer. Under cross-examination later on, Cronjé said that he'd befriended Sunil on his tours to the subcontinent; they even went out to dinner a couple of times, but he only ever spoke to Sunil on tours to India.

And what were their conversations about? 'It was about what blokes normally would talk about. It was cricket, it was politics, it was television and it was whatever blokes talk about normally.' A strange friendship, one has to say: Cronjé doesn't know his surname, but they go out to dinner and talk about things like television? One wonders: Indian television, or South African television?

At around the same time as the first offer by Sunil (i.e. the 1996 tour to India), Hansie Cronjé was also approached by one Mukesh ('MK') Gupta. The introduction was facilitated by ex-Indian captain Mohammed Azharuddin. MK immediately offered Cronjé $30,000 in cash if the Proteas went on to lose the third test in the Kanpur test, where they were already in a desperate situation. 'Money for nothing'; Cronjé accepted.

Yes, this was a fresh slice of salami, but Cronjé probably didn't have a choice but to reveal it. The reason for this was that it had been the same MK Gupta who made the Mumbai offer; the one that the team ended up discussing a few days later. Obviously, Cronjé could expect questions about who had made that offer, and once the identity of that person was revealed, there was a good chance that such a person could be invited to testify at some later point. So, it was probably not a bad idea to disclose as much as possible about the relationship with Mr. Gupta.

There was a further slice of salami concerning Gupta: for a few months after the 1996 tour to India, Cronjé fed him information.

In return for this, MK transferred the equivalent of $50,000 into Cronjé's bank account. Another transfer at around the same time, equating to a further $30,000, was found in Cronjé's account after his statement to the King Commission had been prepared. Cronjé was unsure about the source of this money, but assumed it could also have come from Gupta.

Bronwyn Wilkinson had earlier mentioned the name of one Marlon Aronstam. Hansie Cronjé would proceed to cut some salami relating to this individual and the role that he had played in the innings forfeiture in the Centurion test. Aronstam, a professional bookmaker, had approached Cronjé and offered him a gift as well as a donation to charity, if the declaration and innings forfeiture took place. Cronjé would eventually receive a total of R53,000 and a leather jacket from Aronstam; the donation to charity never happened. The money paid to Cronjé was said to be in respect of future information that Cronjé would provide to Aronstam, but the arrangement would last less than two months.

Oh yes, there was also the R50 bet at the time of the Centurion test, about which Strydom told the commission. Check. According to Cronjé, the only other cricket bet that he'd ever placed was on South Africa to win the World Cup; a bet of one pound, at odds of 4:1.

Towards the end of Cronjé's statement he spoke about the resolve that he eventually managed to build up and the fact that he managed to resist Hamid and Sanjay during the Sharjah Cup, immediately after the tour to India. He also declined another offer of $200,000 in Sharjah.

Hansie Cronjé left the hall after forty minutes. The Commission adjourned shortly thereafter. It was an early end to proceedings, and a long weekend lay ahead.

* * * * *

The King Commission only reconvened six days later, Wednesday, 21 June 2000.

Before Hansie Cronjé took the stand again on this seventh day of hearings, there was testimony by Dr Ian Lewis, a psychiatrist who had been treating Cronjé. Dr Lewis told the Commission that Cronjé had been suffering from clinical depression, 'a major depressive disorder', and that medication had been prescribed.

Dr Lewis further provided details of 'seven or eight of the nine criteria' for this condition of which Cronjé had shown symptoms: a depressed mood and irritability; loss of concentration; loss of pleasure and interest in things; low energy and fatigue; a sense of worthlessness; thoughts of death and dying; loss of appetite; and insomnia.

In spite of this, Dr Lewis believed Hansie Cronjé would be capable of giving evidence, and he did not think that the condition would interfere with Cronjé's ability to tell the truth.

At last, it was time for Hansie Cronjé's cross-examination.

Just before it started, however, Judge Edwin King expressed his concern about a suggestion he had found in Cronjé's statement, that it contained '… the whole truth, limited by the terms of reference'. A debate followed between the judge and Cronjé's legal counsel, with Judge King insisting that he hadn't prejudged the issue. Two days later, the Commissioner would say the following before the questioning continued:

> I am not issuing you a warning, still less is it a threat; it is a friendly reminder. You must assist me and co-operate with me to enable me to make the necessary recommendation to the prosecuting authority.

At the start of Hansie Cronjé's cross-examination there was a lot of discussion about his monetary affairs. In particular, it could be inferred that Cronjé had earned approximately R4 million over a five-year period, just for sponsorships arranged through Clifford Green. (Mr Green is a lawyer who also acts on behalf of the UCBSA.)

Much later, Shamila Batohi would ask Hansie Cronjé whether he wasn't surprised when Marlon Aronstam made a 'gift' of as much as R50,000 to him? To this, Cronjé replied:

> Yes, I was as I said before, I am not trying to boast or to try and be big-headed or anything, but I do have a lot, I don't want to put it in a bad way, but I do have a lot of money, I do deal with people with a lot of money and R50,000 is a big gift and the first R30,000 was a big gift, and I was surprised that he gave me so much, yes, but in my mind, it is not uncommon for the practice that I'm in.

The story unfolds

43

When the 1995 Mandela Trophy approach was discussed, a very interesting observation was made by Hansie Cronjé. According to his testimony, Pat Symcox had said '... it wasn't a big enough figure anyway, and that we shouldn't accept it'. Later on, Cronjé further admitted that they 'probably would have gone through with it', had Pat Symcox been supportive to the offer.

What was also interesting, was that Cronjé said he had never discussed the dealings between himself and MK Gupta with Mohammed Azharuddin, who was the person who had introduced Cronjé and Gupta to one another, and someone with whom Cronjé had a 'very friendly relationship'. (Speaking for myself, I can only say that I will seriously question any friend of mine, if he or she ever puts me in touch with a character who tries to talk me into dubious activities of some sort.)

Cronjé said he did not believe the money he'd accepted from Gupta affected the way that he played in the third test against India, in Kanpur in 1996 (shortly before the team discussion about the offer in the one-day international in Mumbai). But he did concede that it may have affected him subconsciously.

Shamila Batohi asked Hansie Cronjé why he didn't just take the money offered for the Mumbai match himself, without talking to the team like he had in the case of the test match in Kanpur shortly before that, and specifically because South Africa was also extremely unlikely to win the match in Mumbai in any event. Cronjé replied, 'I don't know, I don't know why I didn't accept the money, I probably should have done, and I would have been a richer man for it because it was easy money and you are hundred percent right.' A short while later, Cronjé added, 'I was very annoyed with myself for not taking it, yes.'

Discussing the meeting in which the team deliberated over the Mumbai offer, Hansie Cronjé made the following remark: '... I also made it clear that, in my opinion, if we were going to do it, then the whole team must be in on it. I didn't want to take it, if there were 14 of us in the room, all 14 had to be in, not just 13, but all 14.'

This attitude appears very magnanimous, even if not totally ethical. But it does not tie in with Cronjé's behaviour a few years later, as he admitted to the King Commission, when he'd negotiated $25,000 each for Herschelle Gibbs and Henry Williams to underperform in Nagpur. Yet they were only going to receive $15,000 per person. Why? 'Maybe I was trying to cut something for myself,' Cronjé said in his evidence. At that point, the Commissioner interjected by saying, 'I think, Mr. Cronjé, one must be realistic, I think that is what you were doing?' To this, Hansie Cronjé's response was, 'If that is the way you see it, Judge, I am not going to question you on that.'

In the months following the 1996 tour of India, Hansie Cronjé did, of course, continue to feed MK Gupta with information, including the score around which South Africa would declare in the second innings in the test at Newlands in January 1997 (the test in which Lance Klusener scored a sensational, unbeaten 102 runs from 100 balls).

But then, all of a sudden, Cronjé stopped providing information to Gupta. When Shamila Batohi asked him why this happened, Cronjé responded by saying, 'I felt bad about it because I knew it was wrong to take money for information.'

But this answer of Cronjé's was not consistent with one he had given a day earlier. The focus was on the Centurion test and the discussions that Hansie Cronjé and Marlon Aronstam had had subsequent to that (for example, a forecast provided by Cronjé about the Zimbabwean score in a one-day international against South Africa). Cronjé made the following observation in response to a question from Malcolm Wallace, his own legal counsel: 'Ja, at no stage did I think there was anything wrong with the conversations that I had with Mr. Aronstam …'

Under Shamila Batohi's cross-examination of Hansie Cronjé, with reference to the relationship between Cronjé and Marlon Aronstam, yet another slice of salami would be uncovered.

In prior consultation with Aronstam (who would eventually testify directly after Cronjé), the bookmaker informed Batohi that Hansie Cronjé asked him, the first time that they had ever met, how he (Cronjé) could make money out of cricket. According to Aronstam, his own response was to say that the ball was in Cronjé's court. When Batohi put this to Cronjé, his response was, 'Yes, that could have happened.'

Shortly thereafter, Cronjé admitted that he had also told Aronstam during that same meeting that the game against India in Cochin (some seven weeks later) could be thrown. When Aronstam contacted Cronjé after the second test in India, however, Cronjé told him that the deal was off.

45

Soon after, the two of them stopped having contact. That is, until the scandal broke, at which point they would try and arrange a meeting in order to get their ducks in a row, according to Mr. Aronstam's evidence. But, as Aronstam would later say to the Commission, '…whose ducks did we have to get into a row?'.

Finally, a large part of the cross-examination centred around the relationship with Sanjay Chawla and Hamid Cassim. Hansie Cronjé stuck to his story: Yes, he took money. No, he never had intentions to throw matches, or to approach players in that regard. Yes, he provided information. No, the matches weren't fixed. Yes, he gave in, eventually, under huge pressure and after incessant phone calls, and spoke to some of the players. But no, they didn't go through with it.

As phone call after phone call hunted Hansie Cronjé around the subcontinent, he kept 'spinning Sanjay along'. At least, for 95% of the time he was, according to Cronjé's testimony.

So even if the transcripts of the taped telephone conversations in India were valid, and even if Shamila Batohi could gain access to the tapes and introduce them as evidence before the King Commission, there may still be doubts as to what they really prove …

For those who wanted to feel sorry for Hansie Cronjé, there was ample opportunity to do so.

There was the pathetic image of the ex-captain, who experienced such fright on 7 April 2000 that he 'hid money in different places in the house'. And the same person, throwing away a cellphone for similar reasons.

There was the cricket expert, second to none, admitting, '… in my cricketing opinion, which at this stage is not sought after very highly, I think, around the world …'

And then there was Hansie, for many years the anchor of the national cricket team, the darling of mothers and the hero of schoolboys, breaking down in tears at the end of his testimony.

Could you harden your heart and not feel sorry for the man when his frown turned into a sob?

This was something that should, after all, not happen to any idol. A sports hero is only supposed to weep when he or she is overcome by the momentous occasion of winning an Olympic gold medal and having fifty million people around the world witness, on television, when the victor's anthem is played. The only real heartache that the hero should ever know is that of coming second …

We already knew that Hansie Cronjé was fallible – like the rest of us. And now, perhaps for the first time, some people realised that he was also human – like all of us.

The bookie and the biltong man

Ship out the captain and send in the bookmaker.

Events took a turn towards the bizarre when a sobbing Hansie Cronjé was led out of the hall, and beefy Marlon Aronstam sat down to testify … only to break down in tears, himself, before the first question was asked. Later, he would say that the sight of an emotional Cronjé was just too much for him. After all, he 'respected Hansie as a champion, he was a hero …'

Marlon Aronstam has been involved in the betting 'industry' for 18 years, a bit more than half his life. He once controlled 12.5% of a listed company, he owned racehorses, and he was somebody whom Hansie Cronjé had taken a 'particular liking in' – according to Cronjé himself.

Having started on a low, Mr Aronstam ended up becoming one of the most confident and entertaining witnesses at the King Commission. He had a business-like approach to his testimony and discarded a lot of what others before him had said about betting. He explained exotic bets that were more sophisticated in structure than any over-the-counter derivative that's ever traded. And people believed him. Not only because he spoke with authority, but also because he was, by far, the biggest human being in the room.

A week later, after the Commission had adjourned, there would be further proof of Marlon Aronstam's 'credentials'. At the time, a lot of South Africans were convincing themselves of their country's potential success in its bid to host the 2006 Soccer World Cup. Even the indices on the Johannesburg Stock Exchange (JSE), surged by 10% in a week in anticipation of the big news. Meanwhile, Marlon Aronstam was putting his money on Germany. Publicly. The rest is history. Germany won, and so did Mr. Aronstam. The rest of us were disappointed; the soccer officials even threatened litigation. And, oh yes, the JSE fell by 15%.

Marlon Aronstam explained to the King Commission how easy it was to get access to the captain of the South African cricket team. He obtained the mobile phone number, called him and spoke for two and a half to three minutes, suggesting the Centurion declaration and innings forfeiture. The same evening he met Cronjé – in his hotel room of all places – and convinced him that his image as a captain would be enhanced by such a step. Aronstam was hoping to make some good betting money; a donation to a charity of Cronjé's choice would follow.

But, as so often happens in life, charity began at home. Aronstam found that all betting was closed, and the only person to get anything out of the deal was Hansie Cronjé himself: a gift exceeding R50,000 in cash, said to be in return for future information, pitch reports and the like. A bargain at any price, it seemed. 'Hansie's so knowledgeable, it's frightening,' Aronstam said.

Aronstam didn't think the amount of money that he paid over to Cronjé was that much, not compared to what lawyers earned, in any case. As he said to Hansie Cronjé's legal counsel, '... according to the newspaper this morning ... if you take it into that respect what you guys are earning for a day's work, is that a lot of money?'

By now, the audience had warmed to Marlon Aronstam's sense of humour. Shortly thereafter, he was responsible for one of the comic highlights of the proceedings when he preceded an answer by saying, '... just off the record ...'. He quickly checked himself, realising that everything he said was very much on record before a judicial inquiry and on national television. And then he went on to compare the money that he'd paid over to Hansie Cronjé to the monthly cost of feeding a racehorse.

Marlon Aronstam insisted that he was only ever interested in getting information from Hansie Cronjé. Good information, not only about pitches, but also about the weather, provided him with the competitive edge in his business. He had a list of phone numbers for every single weather bureau around the world. He would phone people at all hours of the day and night to ask about the weather, and he's even gone over to England to watch the weather.

According to Aronstam's evidence, he had a profound influence on South African cricket over the first quarter of the 2000 calendar year. Not only can we thank him for the excitement of the Centurion match, it was also his idea to experiment with Mark Boucher as a pinch hitter at number three, and that South Africa should take on India with a pace attack in their own back yard. The Centurion test was lost and the pinch hitter didn't work out, but the pace attack played a vital part in an historic test series victory in India.

One almost felt sorry for Aronstam when, speaking about suggestions by Hansie Cronjé relating to match-fixing, he said, 'It's easy for me to come here today and tell people that the South African captain had known me for less than one hour, and was telling me that he could throw a game of cricket … Who's going to believe me?'

Aronstam went on to tell the Commission about an internet site where '… they're trying to get percentages of who believes Marlon, who believes Hansie. And the percentages are coming very close …'. It might have been even funnier if it wasn't so sad.

It has to be said, however, that there was at least one set of questions where Mr. Aronstam's line of argument was not totally convincing. In the early part of his testimony he said that he was aware of a recent new rule, approved by the International Cricket Council (ICC), to allow for innings forfeitures in test matches. Yet, in spite of his superior knowledge of the game's intricate details, Aronstam would later say that he wasn't aware of the fact that the ICC's Code of Conduct Commission had been investigating exactly the kind of activities that he'd been engaging in (getting information from players). And he didn't think that he'd actually done anything wrong, in spite of being aware of the fact that Shane Warne and Mark Waugh had received fines for providing information to bookmakers. Marlon Aronstam's testimony came to an end. It was Friday afternoon, 23 June 2000. It was the dead of winter. It had been a dark week for South African sport.

To add insult to injury, the woes would be rounded off the next day, when the Springbok rugby team lost to England. It was only the third time ever that a South African team had suffered this fate in South Africa.

And to top it all, it happened in Bloemfontein – Hansie's home town – of all places.

Talk about a bunch of long faces.

* * * * *

Monday, 26 June 2000. The tenth day of hearings, which would be the last day before the King Commission adjourned.

Only one more witness to go: Hamid 'Banjo' Cassim, sweet-shop owner, roving philanthropist and cricket lover of note. He also happened to be the go-between in Hansie Cronjé's dealings with Sanjay, the bookmaker from India.

For some reason, Cronjé's legal counsel had no intention to cross-examine Mr. Cassim and excused themselves from the day's proceedings.

Strange that they should choose to do that, one can't help thinking. Hamid Cassim was perhaps the most prominent name that Hansie Cronjé had mentioned in his 11 April confession. In the paragraph where he set out how 'it' started, Hansie described how Cassim had told him that he (Cassim) could have made himself some good money if only he had known that the captain was going to declare in the test at Centurion.

When questioned about this incident Cassim himself said he was only joking, as he was no betting man: the last time he placed a bet was in 1976 … and he got a hiding for that!

Hamid Cassim told the Commissioner about his friendships with high-profile cricket players. Firstly, there was Kapil Dev, one of the greatest all-rounders of all time, and the man who led India to their victory in the 1983 World Cup.

Two and a half months after Cassim's testimony before the King Commission, Kapil Dev resigned as coach of the Indian cricket team. At the time he was facing a federal investigation into corruption in cricket. Before that, he had also suffered income tax raids.

Then there was Cassim's relationship with Mohammed Azharuddin, who once gave him a signed shield. Azharuddin was someone who had a lot of things in common with Hansie Cronjé. He was a hard-hitting middle-order batsman, he was a fitness fanatic and he used to captain his country's national cricket team. And, of course, he was implicated in match-fixing allegations. He also happened to be a good friend of Hansie's.

Slightly more than two months after Cassim's testimony before the King Commission, Azharuddin was dropped from the Indian team while under investigation for corruption in cricket.

And then Cassim mentioned some South Africans: Fanie de Villiers, Brian McMillan, Daryll Cullinan, Herschelle Gibbs, Jacques Kallis, Lance Klusener, Paul Adams, Jonty Rhodes, Shaun Pollock, Andrew Hudson … as well as the team manager, Goolam Rajah. And, of course, Hansie Cronjé.

Cassim stated that he had the mobile numbers of a number of players, including Cronjé, implying that this proved the strength of his relationships with the individuals concerned. In addition to being the supplier of biltong to the team, he had also arranged some bargain purchases of electronic goods for one or two of them.

It was interesting to note, however, how the South African players' perceptions relating to the extent of their friendship with Hamid Cassim, differed from Cassim's own version.

In Gibbs's own testimony he said, when speaking about Cassim, 'I've met him once or twice …' When Jacques Kallis was asked whether Cassim was known to him, he said, 'Yes, purely on a sort of a name basis. I don't know him that well.' And Lance Klusener only knew him as 'the biltong man'.

In Hansie Cronjé's initial statement to the King Commission he referred to '… an individual known only as "Hamid". He had been a regular hanger-on around the team …'.

Mr Cassim himself, however, certainly saw matters a little differently. He testified that '… a lot of the South African players have called me, they've given a lot of support to me, and in particular Herschelle Gibbs told me, "Hamid, be strong. We know what type of a character you are …"'.

During Hamid Cassim's cross-examination later on, the nocturnal telephone calls that he had made to Hansie Cronjé were the topic of discussion. Shamila Batohi remarked as follows: 'He was prepared to entertain your calls at that time of the night? You must have been a very, very close friend of his.' To this, Hamid Cassim's response was, 'Yes. Not only him, with all the other players as well.'

Be that as it may. Hamid Cassim testified that one day, out of the blue, he received an overseas phone call from a certain Sanjay Chawla. Cassim couldn't quite remember when this happened; he changed his mind from about the end of January 2000 to the end of November 1999, as the cross-examination evolved.

Not knowing Sanjay from a bar of soap, he agreed to pick him up from the Johannesburg International airport on 30 January 2000. He treated Sanjay to a meal at his business premises, spent the day with him and took him back to the airport. Sanjay flew on to Durban, where South Africa was about to play a one-day international match against Zimbabwe a few days later.

Having known Sanjay for all of one day, Cassim then agreed to neglect his own business commitments and fly to Durban and back a day later. All of this, just so that he could introduce Sanjay to Hansie Cronjé. '... With the goodness of my heart ...' he said to the King Commission. And, '... Sanjay ... wanted to meet Hansie; speak to him about cricket and the love of the game ...'

The introduction took place in Sanjay's room at the Beverley Hills Hotel in Umhlanga Rocks. Having more than gone out of his way to facilitate this meeting, it never 'bothered' Cassim about what Hansie and Sanjay were talking. He just sat in the same room, watching cricket on television. But Cassim did recall hearing them talk about 'scores, pitches, players'. And then Sanjay took an envelope from the safe and gave it to Hansie Cronjé (although Cronjé himself recalled receiving a cellphone box). Cassim told the King Commission, 'I must be very, very honest, I was surprised that Mr. Cronjé took this envelope.'

Although Cassim claimed that it was a sealed envelope given to Hansie by Sanjay, and that he didn't know what it contained, he went on to say: '... if he took it out of the safe it must have contained dollars ...' But why dollars? Hamid Cassim told Shaila Batohi that '... it just came to my mind that it must have been dollars ...'.

After that initial meeting Sanjay Chawla would often call Hamid Cassim if he couldn't get hold of Hansie Cronjé. Cassim would then phone Hansie Cronjé and facilitate contact – at his own expense, and he never got anything in return for it. According to Cassim, this even happened approximately twenty to thirty times during the subsequent tour to India by the South African cricket team.

The biltong man certainly phoned the South African cricket captain a lot. Four or five calls a day often took place, according to phone records presented to the Commission.

But around the time that Sanjay came to South Africa the extent of the contact escalated. On 29 January 2000, the day Sanjay left London, Cassim phoned Cronjé 16 times. Sanjay arrived in South Africa the next morning. Cassim phoned Cronjé 28 times that day. On 31 January there would be a further 13 calls and on 5 February, 12 more – including one at 35 minutes past midnight.

Why? 'I just can't remember, Adv. Batohi,' Cassim said. The Commissioner himself got involved, pointing out that it was only five months before, and suggesting that Cassim needed to think a bit before simply answering that he couldn't explain.

Under cross-examination Hamid Cassim claimed he never knew '... what Mr. Sanjay and Hansie did ...'. Yet, when asked by his own legal counsel whether it was his impression that Hansie Cronjé was 'keeping up a game and making a charade with Sanjay', Cassim said, 'I think so.'

Which also raises the question: why even bother with all those phone calls ... if he thought it was only a charade?

Final thoughts about the Commission

What other issues can one raise in the context of the King Commission?

First and foremost, it needs to be asked why Hansie Cronjé was only asked to testify after so many other people (including eleven other players and ex-players) had testified.

Logic dictates that Cronjé should have taken the stand first. There would then have been the opportunity to test the rigour of his evidence on the basis of everybody else's subsequent testimony. As it happened, Cronjé had the chance to listen to most of the other people before volunteering his own statement.

In this regard, there were a few fundamental pieces of evidence provided by Cronjé himself. In response to a question as to whether he would have revealed the approach to Herschelle Gibbs and Henry Williams had they not 'spilt the beans' before him, his reply was, 'I don't know. I cannot give you an answer on that. Probably not. If – I don't think so.'

Similarly, according to Cronjé himself, he 'probably wouldn't have mentioned' the approach he made to Klusener, Boucher and Kallis before the second test in Bangalore if they hadn't volunteered the information to the commission. The reason?

> ...because since 1994 it's something that the guys have joked about, spoke about. Especially after the meeting in '96, the guys did joke and do talk about it, and laugh about these matters.

Shamila Batohi probably summed the situation up best when she said to Hansie Cronjé, 'So your way of coming clean was just to deal with the allegations against you and not tell the whole truth?' This was in response to Cronjé saying that he only dealt with the Indian tour in his 11 April confession, because he '... was only accused at that stage of the Indian tour'.

Shortly thereafter, Shamila Batohi asked Hansie Cronjé whether it had been his intention to testify last in the proceedings. In fairness, however, this hardly seems like a question that one can put to any witness in the situation in which Cronjé found himself.

When John Dickerson rightly objected on Cronjé's behalf, the Commissioner promptly quelled the issue by saying, 'I think we are making a mountain out of the proverbial molehill. I don't know whatever it is you are endeavouring to extract from the witness, Ms Batohi. Take another route please, if you will.'

At the end of Pieter Strydom's testimony, there was the first bit of uncertainty about some of the intricate rules of the game of cricket.

It all related to the Centurion test. Judge King said to Pieter Strydom, '... in substance, what happened on the fifth day ... this was a one-dayer, was it not?' Shortly thereafter, the judge followed this up as follows: '... although the end result produced a result of a five-day test, it was one side batting and the other side batting ...' Then he concluded by saying, '... the side that scored the most runs was the winner.'

To someone with a cursory understanding of cricket, this reasoning may appear sound enough. But you don't need to be too much of an expert to know that one of the fundamental differences between test cricket and a one-day international is the fact that the former can end in a draw, whereas the latter cannot. In a test, the team that bats last only loses the match if it is bowled out. If, on the other hand, this team finishes with less runs than the opposition, but with any number of wickets intact, the result is a draw. (A draw should, of course, not be confused with a tie, which is the result when two teams end up having the same run total.)

Judge King's statement that '... the side that scored the most runs was the winner', was therefore not accurate: South Africa could have ended with more runs than England at Centurion, but they still had to take the tenth English wicket before it could be said that they had won the match.

Pieter Strydom did not correct the Commissioner. Maybe he just gave him the benefit of the doubt. But the issue would resurface again later, first when Jacques Kallis testified, and twice during Hansie Cronjé's evidence. Addressing Cronjé, Judge King said, '... there is no room for a draw. In fact, there must be a result like in any other one-day game. That is what this was, surely?'

There seemed to be a measure of irritation in Cronjé's response. 'No, this was still a test match, it wasn't a one-day game, Mr. Commissioner, I am sorry to say that to you.'

The Commissioner wasn't going to give up that easily, however. 'We can continue playing on words, but we will hear it from Mr. Aronstam, no doubt.'

But the situation would, thankfully, be cleared up shortly before Marlon Aronstam arrived. When Brendan Manca questioned Cronjé about 'the possibility that one of the teams could have won the game, then', the Commissioner interjected, 'Not could have, would have.' Manca, acting for the UCBSA, jumped at the chance – it seemed as if he'd been waiting for days to clear this one up, champing at the bit. Cronjé witnessed the debate going to and fro between Commissioner and counsel, like a tennis rally, contributing the odd one-worder in between.

'With respect, Mr Commissioner, no. This ... still remained a test match ...' Manca replied, and proceeded with a long and detailed explanation of the issues.

Judge King understood. 'I hear you,' he said.

Finally, the UCBSA seemed to come off very lightly in the first round of the King Commission's hearings.

So what? Surely the UCBSA was not the subject of the Commission;

Hansie Cronjé was. Right?

Wrong.

This was a *Commission of Inquiry into Cricket Match Fixing and Related Matters.* And although the terms of reference were formulated rather narrowly, they certainly extended beyond the scope of just what Mr Cronjé had, or had not, done. Specifically, the terms of reference of the Commission included a point referring to *who was aware of* the proposal 'to the South African cricket team during its tour to India in 1996 that it forfeit or influence the result of a cricket match'.

Dr Ali Bacher testified to the effect that he'd never known about this offer until 'about a few weeks before these revelations emerged in South Africa' (when Hansie Cronjé mentioned it to him fleetingly). Ten days later, Hansie Cronjé's own evidence was that this conversation between himself and the Managing Director of the UCBSA took place '... anywhere between 1996 and 2000'. Probed on this by Shamila Batohi, Cronjé insisted that he was unsure of exactly when the discussion had occurred.

Technically, the responses of Dr Bacher and Mr. Cronjé may not be totally inconsistent. However, in general terms, when you ask somebody about when something happened, few people would be so vague as to say that the event could have occurred any time in the last few years – if, in fact, it occurred in the last few weeks (or even the last few months, for that matter).

But that's not all. The Commissioner asked Hansie Cronjé whether he thought Bob Woolmer would have mentioned the 1996 offer to the UCBSA management. Cronjé responded by saying, 'I speak under correction, but I do believe that Mr. Woolmer has mentioned it to the United Cricket Board.'

Shortly thereafter, Shamila Batohi asked Cronjé whether he was aware that Dr Bacher kept abreast of everything going on in South African cricket. Hansie Cronjé's response was, 'Well, he is the Managing Director, so I take it that he's got a group of people that will inform him of everything that is going on, yes.' This was followed by a question as to whether Cronjé would have expected somebody to have informed Dr Bacher about an incident if it appeared in the newspaper. 'Probably, yes,' was Cronjé's reply.

'... and nothing but the truth'?

When all of this evidence is taken together, it seems clear that Hansie Cronjé believed Dr Ali Bacher had known about the 1996 offer in India for some time (i.e. more than just a few weeks) before the scandal broke.

Based on this, an important question arises. Why did Hansie Cronjé's counsel not challenge Dr Bacher in this regard when he was on the stand?

There is a simple principle in the business world, in terms of which responsibility can be delegated, but accountability cannot. Although it could have been in their client's best interest to do so, Hansie Cronjé's legal counsel did, however, not pursue this line of argument at all by challenging Dr Bacher about preventative measures that the UCBSA might have failed to implement (or enforce properly) over the years.

Only six questions were posed to Dr Ali Bacher by Hansie Cronjé's legal team. This, in spite of the fact that Dr Bacher was in the witness box for a great deal longer than anybody else who testified before Cronjé. And a plethora of issues was raised by Bacher in the process.

Three of the questions put to Dr Bacher by Hansie Cronjé's lawyers concerned death threats that Dr Bacher had received, two of them related to a series of cancelled benefit matches in India in which South African players had been scheduled to take part, and one basically asked whether Dr Bacher had ever had the impression that the South African team were not trying very hard under Cronjé's captaincy. Hardly probing questions, one has to say.

There was also the question put to Hansie Cronjé by Shamila Batohi, about the cricketer's 'relationship with the UCBSA, particularly the management'. Seems like a good question, doesn't it? And relevant, it would appear. It was a question to an ex-employee (who had done something wrong while under an employment contract) about his relationship with the employer.

Cronjé, however, would have nothing of it. He responded passionately:

> I think it will be very dangerous for me at this stage, Mr Commissioner. I don't want to get into a situation where I disclose my relationship with the United Cricket Board, I don't see how that will affect this Commission at all and I think it's very, very unfair for me to comment out of team meetings and out of

the meeting room and the secluded surroundings of Dr Bacher's office. I think it is very unfair at this stage and I don't see any relevance. I am sorry to sound like I don't want to co-operate, but I think it is very unfair on the United Cricket Board and on myself.

He could have just said, 'Bad'. He could have saved himself 112 words. The non-answer was quite telling.

Cronjé got his way; the Commissioner told Shamila Batohi to go to the next question. But what if the line of questioning was allowed? What if Cronjé revealed some of the details about the stormy relationship? It would certainly have been interesting. But it was not to be. What a pity. The big one that got away ...

Subsequent developments

At the end of the same week that the King Commission concluded its first round of hearings, the Protea squad, minus Herschelle Gibbs, left on a two-month tour of Sri Lanka, Australia and Singapore.

On their way out of the country each player was asked to sign the following declaration at a highly publicised press conference:

I declare that I

1. Have never, for personal reward, intended, nor agreed, to act in breach of any rules governing cricket or the ethics of cricket.
2. Have never, for personal reward, furnished information to any party concerning any cricket match, pitch or weather conditions or the likely outcome of any match.
3. Have never personally, or encouraged others to, deliberately play below normal standards.
4. Agree to bring immediately to the attention of the United Cricket Board any approaches, suggestions or knowledge relating to the above matters should I become aware of such information.

I acknowledge that if I should be in breach of any of the above provisions, I could be banned from representative cricket for life and, furthermore, could be subject to an appropriate fine as decided by the United Cricket Board.

I also undertake to ensure that no dishonesty or corruption in any form will take place or affect any match in which I participate.

It was a successful tour for the Proteas. First they drew a three-match test series with the Sri Lankans. Then they went Down Under for three one-day internationals against Australia, at Melbourne's Indoor Colonial Stadium. They lost the first match, tied the second and won the third. Having shared the spoils with the world champions they went to Singapore, where they came out tops in a triangular tournament against New Zealand and Pakistan.

The team did well in spite of all the emotional energy that must have been tapped over the course of the King Commission's proceedings.

And Shaun Pollock came into his own as a captain, even if his own form as a bowler might have been under pressure. His apparent gamble, asking unheralded Andrew Hall to bowl three crucial overs towards the end of the second match in Melbourne, proved to be an inspired decision. It may long be remembered as the defining moment of the Pollock captaincy.

The king is dead. Long live the king.

One week after Hansie Cronjé's tears evoked the nation's sympathy at the King Commission, the news broke that the ex-hero was to engage Max Clifford, a well-known public relations consultant, from the United Kingdom.

Max Clifford is not someone who shies away from a PR challenge. Hansie Cronjé joined an esteemed client list, including the likes of O.J. Simpson and Geoff Boycott.

Clifford would, in future, handle all Cronjé's dealings with the media. And he certainly got busy quickly. Within a month, television interviews were signed up with Australian and South African networks. A series of three programmes, on consecutive nights, was eventually screened by M-Net in South Africa at the end of August 2000. The interviews, alleged to have netted Cronjé not less than R1 million (£100,000), are discussed elsewhere in this book.

Around the same time the rumours about a possible book deal started gaining momentum. Who would get the sweetest deal for Hansie Cronjé: Clive Rice, or Max Clifford? Only time will tell ... but an advance payment of R2,5 million (£250,000) for Cronjé has already been suggested.

According to reports, however, Cronjé decided not to go to London to discuss his future with Clifford, as had been planned at one point. The reason for this related to the risk that Cronjé, once he set foot on English soil, might be arrested and extradited to India, where he was sought for questioning about corruption in cricket.

While Hansie Cronjé was starting to cash in, Herschelle Gibbs, Henry Williams and Pieter Strydom appeared before a disciplinary hearing of the UCBSA, charged with the wrongdoings they had admitted to the King Commission.

Gibbs and Williams pleaded guilty. They were fined and suspended by a three-man tribunal under one Judge King. But this was not the same Judge Edwin King; this was Judge Mervyn King. Ironic, not so?

But Mervyn King was a most appropriate choice, as he was the pre-eminent figure in formulating a set of guidelines for corporate governance in South African business a few years earlier. Because that's exactly what match-fixing over an extended period is: it is, quite simply, bad corporate governance by cricket players (employees who do wrong), as well as bad corporate governance by cricket administrators (employers who fail in their duty to put an end to such wrongdoings). Good corporate governance dictates that those who do wrong should be sanctioned. Better corporate governance suggests that there should be measures in place, either to prevent the wrongdoings in the first place or, failing that, to prevent them from escalating by putting an end to them as soon as the first signs appear.

Gibbs was fined R60,000 (£6,000) and Williams R10,000 (£1,000). Although their initial deeds were not that dissimilar, one of the reasons for the differential in fines related to the fact that Gibbs had initially lied to the UCBSA on more occasions than Williams had.

Gibbs would only be able to play for the South African national side again in the year 2001. And the income foregone (in the form of salaries over the period of the suspension, match fees, performance bonuses as well as sponsorships) would be a large multiple of his fine. Added to this the cost of legal counsel, both for purposes of his appearance before the King Commission and the disciplinary hearing, and the small mistake of listening to his captain in Nagpur would end up costing him close to R1 million (£100,000).

In Williams's case the direct cost would, at first glance, appear to have been less extreme. He was no longer a youngster, and his international career was probably over. But he was about to commence with a benefit season at Boland ... and obviously his attraction as a marketable commodity would be seriously dented in the process. If Hansie Cronjé had never entered his room in Nagpur, Williams and those people proposing toasts at his benefit banquets would have reflected on a career of toil that could, eventually, have translated into success: a career that would go from disadvantaged beginnings in the Cape's wine-making areas to the ultimate highlight, when he was able to represent his country on the world stage. Now, everyone at the banquet would look at him and be reminded of the match-fixing debacle. That is, if he would be able to sell tickets for the banquet in the first place ...

And Pieter Strydom? Well, he was found not guilty: the official line being that no bet was placed, after all. The fact that he not only had serious intentions to place a bet, but that he also acted on these intentions – and that he was prevented only for reasons relating to a third party – evidently counted as lesser arguments.

The King Commission released its long-awaited interim report at the end of August 2000. A rather cumbersome document, the report summarised the evidence and quoted substantial portions from the cross-examining of the various witnesses.

One of the more incisive points from the report was that some of the facts, as presented to the Commission, were 'not readily reconcilable with the notion of Cronjé spinning Sanjay along'.

The report also stated, 'It is interesting, that the first time Cronjé was approached to fix a match, he was prepared to and did entertain the suggestion.'

But there were no real findings yet; those would have to wait for the second round of hearings.

At the time of writing, the King Commission has not resumed the second round of hearings. However, upon the resumption of the hearings in November 2000, its most important item of business would be to deal with any new evidence that Shamila Batohi might have been able to gather on her trip to India in September 2000. Would we hear the taped telephone conversations? Or would we only see comprehensive transcripts, authenticated by the Indian officials? Whatever the answer, the South African Minister of Sport seems to think that the new evidence could be exciting.

What about the possibility that new names might be pulled out of the hat? For example, other South African players who might not have been under any sort of suspicion before? It should be borne in mind that we only ever saw excerpts from the transcripts. Should we perhaps brace ourselves for any new shocks?

And would anything new come out of Hansie Cronjé's bank details? Ultimately, the phone conversations, by themselves, would probably not prove to be conclusive, based on Cronjé's own theory of 'spinning them along' (although the judge had already signalled that he didn't really buy into this explanation).

Finally, would any new witnesses appear from out of the woodwork and testify to the Commission, adding to our understanding of the complex web of deceit?

Ultimately, Judge King will basically tell us three things:

Firstly, the circumstances relating to the periods and incidents included in the terms of reference will be explained. Importantly, this will include an analysis of who exactly was aware of all the incidents. In addition to the individuals who were directly involved, it will be interesting to see how the judge's thoughts develop with regards to the UCBSA's knowledge of the team discussion around the 1996 Mumbai offer. In his interim report he said the following: 'It is not at this stage clear whether, or when, it also came to the knowledge of the team management or the United Cricket Board.'

Secondly, the judge has a responsibility to make recommendations concerning the various matters falling in its mandate. He will suggest control mechanisms, the intention of which will be to ensure that corruption in South African cricket is stamped out as far as is humanly possible.

Thirdly and, according to many people, perhaps most significantly, Judge King will have to rule on Hansie Cronjé's prospective indemnity from prosecution. This will be based on whether the judge thought Cronjé made a full disclosure, and that he was honest and truthful in every aspect. Or was there likely to be a few more hidden slices of the truth salami?

2

The Afrikaner connection

Stabilis, according to my Oxford Latin Mini-dictionary, means firm, steady, stable, lasting, immovable or constant. Strong words indeed, and all terms that most of us would have ascribed to Hansie Cronjé once.

Stabilis is the motto of Grey College, the third oldest school in South Africa and Hansie Cronjé's alma mater. Founded in 1855 in Bloemfontein, it is today widely regarded as one of the top schools in the country.

How do you know that someone was schooled at Grey? Well, first of all he will tell you. Without exception, old boys take tremendous pride in their Grey heritage.

Then there is the handshake. Instead of offering all four fingers (thumb pointing upward) as is generally considered appropriate in most of Western society, people from Grey offer each other middle and index finger only, gripping those of the other party with the remaining two fingers.

And last but not least, there is the personality. Grey old boys are generally known as gregarious, confident and well-rounded individuals. In short, they are solid citizens. More often than not, they are clear leaders in whatever situation they happen to find themselves. *Stabilis*.

This personality is cultivated from the very first day that new pupils set foot at Grey: they are taught to believe that they are something special; that they can achieve all they ever set out to.

The statistics do, after all, speak for themselves. More than ninety sportsmen from the school have reached the highest level by representing their country over the years. The school has also produced two heads of state, several judges, famous writers and captains of industry aplenty.

Not only are they justifiably proud of their boys, they also stand by them. Go to the Grey website today and look at the page of famous old Greys, and amongst the top six sportsmen listed you will still find the entry 'Hansie Cronjé, former South African cricket captain'. Disgraced maybe, but still an achiever – and forever one of them.

Hansie Cronjé is not the first Grey old boy to be shrouded in some measure of controversy. When one considers the combination of intellect and leadership to have emanated from the school over the years, it is to be expected, for example, that some dissenting voices in South Africa's troubled political landscape would have come from Grey. And in a country which used to be as intolerant of ideological opposition as South Africa, these characters couldn't be anything but controversial.

Take Bram Fischer (class of 1925, first-team tennis, also played rugby), for example. The grandson of a Prime Minister of the Orange River Colony and son of a judge-president of the Orange Free State, many believed that this old Grey was destined to be a successful National Party politician in the 1950s. He chose, however, to 'go the other way' and achieved fame as Nelson Mandela's advocate in the Rivonia Trial. He was eventually tried and sentenced to life imprisonment for conspiracy to commit sabotage himself. In his book, *Long Walk to Freedom*, Mandela pays Fischer the following tribute:

> **As an Afrikaner whose conscience forced him to reject his own heritage and be ostracized by his own people, he showed a level of courage and sacrifice that was in a class by itself.**

Controversial perhaps, but *stabilis* for sure.

Grey College has a traditional but forward-looking approach. Perhaps this was why boys in the 60s and 70s who came from homes that fostered a deep respect for their Afrikaner heritage, found themselves playing a sport that was historically the sport of the English.

In those days cricket was only just starting to take root amongst Afrikaners. The all-conquering national teams of the 1960s (the last decade of pre-isolation sport in South Africa) consisted solely of English speakers. Even Peter Laurence van der Merwe, highly rated South

African captain in the mid 1960s, could hardly speak Afrikaans – this in spite of his surname not only being one of the most common Afrikaans family names, but in fact also the name popularly attached to the Afrikaans version of the village idiot: the butt of all jokes.

In the early phase of Peter van der Merwe's international career, he played for the South African team in the 1964/65 home test series against England. Hendrik Verwoerd, the 'architect of apartheid' and a staunch Afrikaner Nationalist with comparatively little support from the English community at the time, was Prime Minister. In a famous incident, Verwoerd was once told the lunchtime score during a test match – the English were batting. '*Whose* English?', he was reported to have asked, '*Their* English or *our* English?' Few other stories could ever epitomise the cricket divide – but also the uncomfortable bond – between Afrikaner Government and English Opposition in a bygone South African era any better.

Enter Johan Volsteedt. Son of a former Grey College principal who was a rugby man to the core, the younger Volsteedt had developed a preference for cricket by the time he commenced with his teaching career at Grey in 1971. No doubt Volsteedt Junior was spurred on by his countrymen's series of huge victories against the touring Australians less than a year earlier: South Africa had won those four tests by 170 runs, an innings and 129 runs, 307 runs and 323 runs respectively. But there were no Afrikaners in the national team. Not yet, anyway.

Fortunately for Volsteedt he not only had an important point to prove, he also had good material to work with. Around the same time that he started teaching and coaching cricket at Grey College, a boy named Kepler Christoffel Wessels started his high school career. 'Kepler', it has to be said, is a rather unique name; 'Christoffel' as Afrikaans as they come.

As an impressionable twelve-year-old, Wessels had also witnessed the drubbing handed out to the 1970 Australian tourists. And that's all the motivation he needed to focus his energy; he'd already proven to himself and the outside world that he possessed an abundance of talent. The Volsteedt-Wessels partnership was consummated.

Over the next five years, the unassuming teacher-coach with the passion for the Englishman's game and the reserved schoolboy prodigy with the dogged tenacity, conspired to change the face of cricket at Grey

College – and eventually South Africa – forever. Wessels would expect Volsteedt to throw balls at him at all hours, even in the off season when the only time for training sessions was in the mornings before school – subzero temperatures to boot. To anyone who hasn't been to Bloemfontein in winter this may not mean much, but let the record show that it's by far South Africa's coldest city when the mercury drops.

The teacher's tremendous patience and understanding was called on in other areas as well. Kepler didn't have much time to 'waste' on the academic side of things; there was, after all, an international cricket career beckoning and he had to train. This meant that homework had to be outsourced to the rest of the Wessels family. Volsteedt, not only the cricket coach but also the Afrikaans teacher, remembers writing at the bottom of one of Kepler's essays: 'Tell your Mom this is one of her better efforts.'

The early years of establishing a Grey College brand of cricket were not easy. Kepler Wessels made a huge impact, but one swallow does not a summer make. In those days, one-day rules did not apply to schoolboy matches, so games could be drawn. Johan Volsteedt speculates that the burden Wessels volunteered to take on, protecting his side from defeat when he wasn't able to spur them on to victory, may have influenced the Wessels style forever after. This could explain why the player ended up with a reputation for being conservative rather than adventurous, deliberate rather than stylish.

Kepler Wessels not only rewrote the record books at Grey College, he also represented Free State Schools for five years in a row and South African Schools for three years, the last as captain. In retrospect he could be called the 'Tiger Woods' of South African cricket. Except that Tiger Woods hadn't been born yet.

In one of life's great ironies, the Afrikaner boy who had wanted nothing more than to represent his country at the highest level, ended up playing test cricket for Australia before he played for South Africa. The political storms of the 1970s were brewing, sports isolation was really starting to bite, and Kepler Wessels didn't have time to sit around. He needed to play international cricket and he needed to do so fast; Australia was prepared to give him that opportunity. The left-hander would eventually play 40 test matches (24 for Australia and 16 as captain of South Africa), score 162 on debut against England in the 1982/83 season and end up with a test average of 41.00. No slouch with the bat, one can say with some measure of safety.

Fast forward seven years. Enter Hansie Cronjé. By now, Grey College had established itself as a force in cricket, much like it had already been for many decades in the game of rugby. When Hansie started playing for the school's first cricket team as a charismatic fifteen-year old, the whole mindset had thus progressed from 'never wanting to lose' to 'always believing we can win'. Once again, Volsteedt believes that this might have something to do with the more flamboyant batting style as well as the assertive captaincy that Cronjé would exhibit in future years.

The special bond between Hansie Cronjé and Johan Volsteedt is well documented. In one of the best-known anecdotes, Hansie (while still at school) promised Volsteedt that he would fly the teacher to the UK one day, when – not *if* – he played in his first test for South Africa at Lord's. That day arrived seven years later, and true to Cronjé's promise, the mentor was indeed there. Interestingly, the generosity exhibited by Cronjé on this occasion flies in the face of his own testimony before the King Commission that he wasn't overly generous to his friends (to the point of seldom buying them a drink, for example).

Johan Volsteedt continued coaching Hansie Cronjé after the latter had left school: Volsteedt became Free State coach in 1989, shortly after Cronjé had started playing for his province. The coach soon inspired the young team to their first limited-overs trophy and recalls with pride that the team in those days used to include up to eight old Greys. A couple of years later, Volsteedt handed over the coaching reins to Eddie Barlow.

Kepler Wessels and Hansie Cronjé are not the only two prominent Afrikaner cricketers to list Johan Volsteedt as their mentor. In his autobiography entitled *White Lightning*, Allan Donald recognises Volsteedt's early influence on his career. Donald, who was only at Grey College for two years, tells how Volsteedt drummed it into him and his team-mates 'that to succeed in sport, you had to be as mentally and physically strong as Kepler Wessels'.

Johan Volsteedt has since followed in the footsteps of his father as the Principal of Grey College. When I eventually met with him in his office, the photograph taken on the ground at Lord's showing Volsteedt and his two favourite sons – Kepler Wessels and Hansie Cronjé, successive captains of South Africa – was still exhibited with much pride right next to his chair. Taken on the 21st of July 1994 when he was Hansie's guest, it's framed together with the ticket for the Compton Stand – itself a collector's item, because the MCC made the interesting *faux pas* of still depicting the old South African flag. It happened to be two months after the inauguration of President Nelson Mandela, but the Old Country was a bit slow in recognising the New South Africa.

The meeting with Johan Volsteedt was one of the most interesting I had in writing this book. I was introduced to him by a friend who was head boy (or school captain, as they call it) of Grey a few years after Hansie Cronjé. The first phone call was quite tough. The Principal sounded rather dour; he didn't seem particularly keen to speak to me and was at pains to point out that Hansie was a friend of his. The extent of the friendship is illustrated by the fact that Volsteedt was Master of Ceremonies at Hansie and Bertha's wedding five years ago; he also proposed the toast to the bridal couple that day.

'Fine, Mr Volsteedt,' was my response, 'even if you only want to say good things about the man, I still would like to meet with you.' I was, after all, trying to be objective.

So, Johan Volsteedt agreed to see me. I could sense this was going to be one of the more difficult meetings. Prepare twenty questions, I thought, this time you're going to need it. No-one said writing a book is meant to be easy.

Arriving at Grey's main administrative building, two plaques were in evidence in the foyer. The one acknowledges the founder of the school, Sir George Grey, 'Soldier – Statesman – Explorer – Administrator'. The other commemorates the inauguration of restorations to the building under the auspices of one Ewie Cronjé, Chairman of the Grey College Reunion, 1985 – just in case you needed any confirmation that Hansie Cronjé and his family counted for something in the broader Grey College setup.

I sat down to chat with Johan Volsteedt. After a few minutes of introduction and innocuous small talk, he broke into traditional Afrikaner hospitality, offering to buy me breakfast. Perhaps this wasn't going to be so difficult after all?

He began telling me about his life as an educator, about 47 years of involvement with The School, about 145 years of Grey College history, and about some of the special kids that he'd seen come and go over the years. How many other teachers will ever coach five captains of South African Schools cricket teams? And he isn't even finished yet.

There's no denying Johan Volsteedt's Afrikaner status. But would it be fair to imply that Grey College is essentially an Afrikaans school? Perhaps not entirely – the school's home page on the internet (yes, it's got one, and rather elaborate at that) refers proudly to its parallel-medium status in the mission statement. Curiously, this mission statement appears on the main page next to a picture of the school's tuck shop of all places. But then again: how many schools can say that their tuck shop is a national monument? In Grey's case, the quaint tin construction which served as a hospital in the Anglo-Boer War is one of five buildings awarded this accolade of significance and protection.

About a third of Grey's pupils receive their instruction in English today. Many of the famous old boys were indeed English-speaking, including a number of editors of prominent English newspapers – people like Joel Mervis, Peter Sullivan and René de Villiers. But when you analyse the language profile of the school over time, a clear trend emerges. Started by Sir George Grey in 1855, the early history was predominantly English. As the demographics of Bloemfontein started changing, however, the school started becoming increasingly Dutch and from around the turn of the 19th century, Afrikaans. With two-thirds of the schoolboys and nearly 90% of the teachers Afrikaans-speakers today, it is therefore probably not unfair to describe the school as predominantly Afrikaans.

Discussing the language and cultural make-up, Volsteedt was adamant about the double-medium status. 'It's vitally important to us,' he said on a number of different occasions. He further speculated that Grey had more alumni participating on both sides of the Anglo-Boer War than any other school in the country. Given the school's size and demographic history, this is probably true. Importantly, however, the school prides itself on its tolerance. A government school, it opened its doors to all races the day the country's laws changed in 1993 – the same year that Johan Volsteedt became Principal. When I asked him how many black pupils there were at the moment, his dry sense of humour came through. 'Government also keeps asking me that racist question; and I just say that, being Grey, we are squarely between black and white here.' Having been there, however, I can testify that the school has a very New South African look and feel to it. And a pleasant mood of tolerance was very much in evidence.

We eventually turned to the Hansie Cronjé issue. Knowing how close Volsteedt and Cronjé were – and in fact still are – and realising how much of an outsider I am in this matter, I felt rather like the evening I asked my father-in-law for my wife's hand. All along you realise the conversation has to get there eventually, but somehow you contrive to put off the inevitable for as long as possible.

Volsteedt talked about his early memories of Cronjé as a schoolboy. By all accounts he was a model pupil who excelled not only at sport but also academically (dispelling Cronjé's remarks at the King Commission that his wife was the brainy one in the family). Importantly, he had a way with people and he was an exceptional link between personnel and pupils – a precursor to the role he would one day play in the fragile relationship between cricket players and those who administered the game.

But Cronjé could also be quite a 'naughty bugger'. Volsteedt recalled fondly how the school team went on a cricket tour to Natal once and captain Cronjé organised wake-up calls for the coach and all the other players at four o'clock in the morning. Hansie himself, meanwhile, was sleeping soundly. Other anecdotes like that, I asked? Not many, the answer came slowly. Hansie had his moments, but you wouldn't really call him a barrel of laughs.

I braced myself to ask The Dreaded Question: how did Volsteedt feel when he heard about Hansie Cronjé's confession on 11 April? The Principal paused and collected himself.

Shock, yes. Disappointment, definitely. 'The worst of all,' he said, 'is that I always made a point of coaching the boys with values very much in mind.

'As a coach, I tried to teach them about life more than about the sport. You see, there was never really time to do that kind of thing in the classroom … Yes, Hansie knows how I feel; we've spoken about it.'

When Volsteedt started philosophising, the look in his eyes and the tone of his voice both deepened. He quoted slowly but perfectly from the first page of an old Grey's biography by Stephen Clingman, called *Bram Fischer – Afrikaner Revolutionary*. The passage spoke of the transient and delicate nature of a life as it passes through time and space.

Volsteedt gave me the book from which he'd quoted. I read and re-read the piece a few times. Eventually I realised that this was his way of

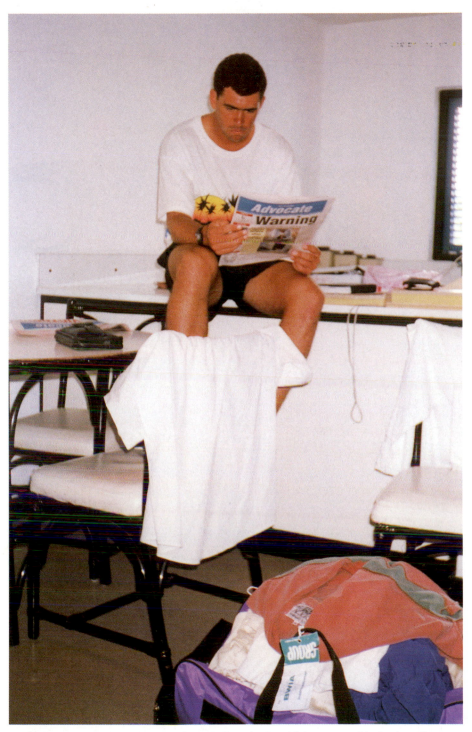

Whiling away time on tour: Hansie reading the local Advocate *with the headline 'Warning' – in retrospect a rather ironic omen.*

The idyllic side of touring – Hansie Cronjé in the West Indies, 1992. Corrie van Zyl, Dave Richardson, Mike Procter and Mark Rushmere are in the background.

Mark Rushmere, Kepler Wessels, Hansie Cronjé, Jonty Rhodes and Tertius Bosch in Jamaica, 1992. Alan Jordaan is in the background.

Hansie Cronjé, Johan Volsteedt and Kepler Wessels at Lord's, 21 July 1994.
Volsteedt (currently the Principal of Grey College, Bloemfontein) coached both of
these South African captains when they were at school.

Hansie Cronjé on the cellphone, with bus driver Hugh Jones and captain Kepler
Wessels (Manchester, 1994).

South African tour party to England, Scarborough 1994.
Back: Craig Matthews, Richard Snell, Allan Donald, Tim Shaw, Fanie de Villiers, Gerhardus Liebenberg, Kepler Wessels, Mike Procter, Andrew Hudson, Peter Kirsten, Craig Smith.
Front: Brian McMillan, Fritz Bing, Daryll Cullinan, Jonty Rhodes, Goolam Rajah, Dave Richardson, Hansie Cronjé.

Sleeping next to Craig Matthews after a most successful triangular tournament in Pakistan (against Pakistan and Australia). Cronjé had a purple patch, scoring 354 runs in 6 matches for an average of 88.5.

Hansie Cronjé and Bob Woolmer: the captain-coach bond at its strongest (Hamilton, New Zealand, February 1995).

South African President Nelson Mandela and South African cricket captain Hansie Cronjé (Ysterplaats, New Year's Day 1996).

Hansie the athlete (1996 World Cup, Karachi).

The captain sets an example – picking up the shells after clay pigeon shooting (1996 World Cup, Rawalpindi).

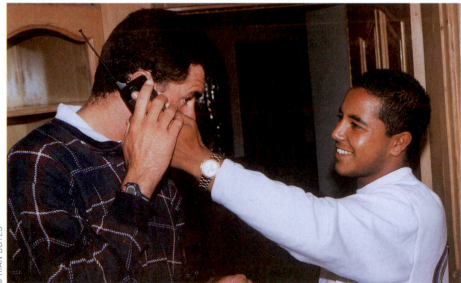

On the cellphone again ... this time with Paul Adams (World Cup 1996, Pakistan).

Not allowed to play on a drenched field: Gary Kirsten and Hansie Cronjé, with Jonty Rhodes stretching (before the World Cup match against the UAE at Rawalpindi, 1996).

Man of the Match against New Zealand after scoring 78 off 64 balls with 11 fours and 3 sixes (1996 World Cup, Faisalabad).

Hansie Cronjé and Mohammed Azharuddin the day before the Wanderers test, January 1997. Azharuddin was one of the prominent names mentioned by Cronjé in his testimony before the King Commission. According to Cronjé, the two of them 'just clicked'.

The captain standing out – singing the national anthem before the one-day international against Zimbabwe at the Wanderers, January 1997. (Andrew Hudson, Rudi Bryson, Paul Adams, Daryll Cullinan, Hansie Cronjé, Adam Bacher, Jacques Kallis, Pat Symcox, Shaun Pollock, Gary Kirsten, Allan Donald)

Standing ovation for Jonty Rhodes reaching his century at Lord's, 19 June 1998.

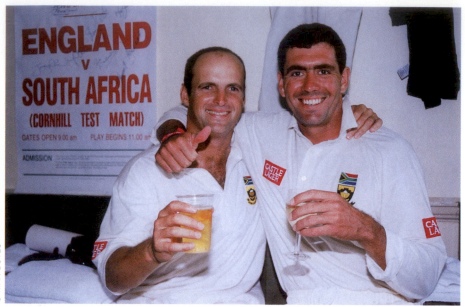

Gary Kirsten and Hansie Cronjé after winning the second test by 10 wickets at Lord's on the fourth day of the match, 21 June 1998. In the top left corner can be seen how Pat Symcox had scratched out the 'FIVE-DAY MATCH' and changed it to 'FOUR DAYS' ... before the match (based on what had happened in 1994).

In the slips – versus Derbyshire at Derby, July 1998.
(Jonty Rhodes, Hansie Cronjé, Jacques Kallis, Daryll Cullinan).

Hansie Cronjé benefit golf day, Sun City, 1997.

Hansie Cronjé salutes the crowd after reaching his century against England (Trent Bridge, Nottingham, 23 July 1998). This was Cronjé's sixth (and last) test century, and the only one in a match that South Africa did not go on to win. Shaun Pollock congratulates him.

Alec Stewart and Hansie Cronjé in the post-match interview after the Trent Bridge test, 1998.

Hansie Cronjé smiles in disbelief after being given out LBW in the test against England at Headingley, Leeds (August 1998). This was the test involving umpire Javed Akhtar of Pakistan, where a large number of dubious LBW decisions were given (8 against South Africa, 2 against England).

Poise and balance – versus England at Edgbaston in the triangular tournament also involving Sri Lanka (August 1998).

A pensive coach and captain – each busy with their own thoughts during the one-day international versus Sri Lanka, Trent Bridge (August 1998).

Hansie Cronjé congratulates Daryll Cullinan after taking his first test wicket ever – against West India at Centurion Park, January 1999. This test completed the 5-0 series whitewash and the winning margin of 351 runs was the largest defeat ever (by runs) of any West Indies team.

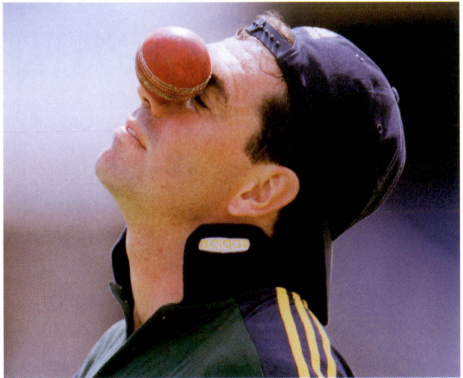

The captain keeps his eye on the ball.

making peace with the Hansie Cronjé affair. I identified the role of mentorship, the qualities of the individual and the importance of outside forces in the quote.

In addition to the serious stuff, the Principal also had one-liners up his sleeve for every occasion. 'Comparing cricket to any other game is like comparing chess to snakes and ladders,' he said in partial response to a question about Cronjé's ability to read the game.

'When money talks, even the angels listen,' Volsteedt continued, when asked why he thought Hansie might have done what he did. 'In the end,' he added, 'it all probably became a bit too easy.'

Which brings us to the official Grey College response to the whole affair – as formulated by Johan Volsteedt. 'We condemn the deed, but we will never condemn the person.'

Volsteedt told me about the day after the big news broke. He made a speech in the school hall, explaining this point of view. It is the custom that all hall gatherings end with the official school song, followed by the school's war cry. That day, after Volsteedt had closed off a highly emotional speech, the boys went through the motions of singing the school song. But nobody felt like doing any war cry – all those present must have found the whole experience just too draining. Nothing had been arranged; it simply didn't happen. For about twenty seconds, which in the context must have felt like an eternity, there was just stunned silence.

Then, from the middle of the hall a lone voice risked a familiar tune. 'Hansie is my hero …' he started hesitantly but bravely, only to be joined moments later by a thousand and ninety-nine other boys, '…we shall not be moved! HANSIE IS OUR HERO, WE SHALL NOT BE MOVED!!' And louder still … the refrain thundering around the building.

When the song ended, there was hardly a dry eye in the room. Volsteedt felt vindicated: the boys had confirmed his message. He went to his office and phoned Hansie Cronjé to tell him what had happened. 'Today you should have been here,' he told his protégé. And Volsteedt vowed that Hansie would indeed be back to address the hall gathering one day.

As Johan Volsteedt was telling me that story, I was covered in goose bumps. I could sense the emotional energy and I was immediately taken back to my own education at a boys' school which – although less prestigious than Grey College – was also proud of its traditions. I actually think it's got something to do with the very fact of being a boys' school: the culture is different, the vibe is different, the pupils just relate to each other in a way which is probably not possible if you mix the sexes at that very sensitive age.

I tested the boys' school theory with Volsteedt. 'I don't really know,' he said, 'but I do think the competitive spirit here is a lot stronger than in other schools. That's another reason why it's so difficult to come to terms with the Hansie episode.'

Talking about the regular outside speakers at the school's hall gatherings, Volsteedt proudly recalled the day that President Nelson Mandela addressed the boys – seemingly the most special memory of his life at Grey. He showed me where Madiba signed the visitors' book: 'Visiting Grey College has been an unforgettable experience, 28 November 1997.' This time it was Volsteedt's turn to get goose bumps – 'like when you told me the *Hansie is our hero* story,' I remarked. 'Yes, except that Mandela doesn't have flaws.'

Johan Volsteedt offered to take me on a school tour, he offered to buy me a custard slice at the tuck shop, he offered to lend me the photograph taken at Lord's, he took me to the library and asked the librarian to help me look at old school annuals in which Hansie Cronjé featured. He took me into the school hall and showed me the inscriptions of Hansie Cronjé's name on five different boards. One board had a Latin heading: *Nihil Stabile Quod Infidum*. I racked my brain for my schoolboy Latin, but eventually Volsteedt offered to translate: 'Nothing is steadfast which is not true.' The sad irony of the phrase was not lost on either of us.

Volsteedt took me into his home and introduced me to his wife. She was lying down, watching television – recuperating from an operation. 'You know, I don't get up early to watch the cricket anymore,' he said as we left the room. Quite a telling comment.

He showed me a huge poster in his home study: action photograph, Hansie batting, personalised, inscribed with the Lord Harris monograph: 'You do well to love Cricket, for it is more free from anything sordid, anything dishonorable …' He shook his head as we started walking back to the office.

I couldn't have been more mistaken about the difficult meeting. But don't get me wrong: the Principal is not a walkover. Everywhere we went, the boys got up when we approached – whether in the classroom, the tuck shop or around the recreation fields. And I somehow didn't think it was out of respect for *me*. There's no doubt who's in charge here.

My meeting with Johan Volsteedt started at half past eight in the morning; when I eventually left his office it was three and a half hours later.

As the plane took off I realised that, in my quest to better understand Hansie Cronjé's fall from grace and *stabilis*, I had only managed to confuse myself further. Surely, whatever went wrong happened in spite of 'the Bloemfontein, Afrikaner thing' and not because of it?

As the Free State capital finally disappeared in the distance, my final thoughts returned to Johan Volsteedt. What a gentleman, I thought. And how sorry I felt not only for him, but also for hundreds of thousands of people like him – Afrikaners and others alike – who felt personally let down by the whole Hansie Cronjé saga.

* * * * *

Max du Preez described himself as a barefoot country boy who misunderstood the universe completely and was only ever sure of one thing: Don Quixote was the ultimate role model. As a result, he left a scrap yard of damaged windmills in his wake. When he became unemployable by the mainstream press after fifteen years as a journalist, he started his own newspaper and was soon sued for defamation by the state president, three police generals, an attorney general and several other prominent, honest citizens. The one case he lost closed down his newspaper, and he triumphantly joined the post-liberation public broadcaster as a television anchor – just to be fired unceremoniously because the new ruling elite had never heard of Don Quixote. At present, he is licking the wounds of his unremarkable life and is thoroughly enjoying himself as an independent producer of documentary films, columnist, energetic purveyor of nonsense and spectacularly unsuccessful farmer in the Eastern Free State.

Du Preez is nothing if not an Afrikaner. With an Afrikaans name, an Afrikaans accent, even an Afrikaans appearance (beard included, as well as bakkie, with canopy), there's little potential for any mistaken identity here. Yet the percentage of Afrikaners who have willingly associated with him and his published views over the last two decades have been a relatively small minority, limited to the precious few who started rejecting rebel tours and the *Broederbond* long before it actually became fashionable to do so. Some of his views are simply ahead of their time; others seem so outrageous that we cannot bear the thought of agreeing with them just in case the man is actually proven right.

Within twenty-four hours of Hansie Cronjé's first confession, Max had written a piece entitled 'Woe is the volk: Hansie goes out for a buck' which was published in the newspaper *Business Day* two days later. To fully appreciate the Du Preez vernacular, the reader would probably need to have spent more than the odd summer holiday around the Garden Route or the Kruger National Park. But even a non-South African would be likely to find his self-deprecating style and his tongue-in-cheek analysis insightful and entertaining. In closing this chapter, I couldn't think of a more succinct piece than this to summarise the Afrikaner agony contained in the Hansie Cronjé saga:

> It was not a memorable time. I was an ordinary 15-year-old Vrystaatse Boerseun from Kroonstad with a shaved head and short pants. My life consisted of the dominee, rugby, strict discipline and an excruciatingly dull school.
>
> But I remember September 6 1966 very clearly. I came home from school to find my family home eerily quiet. My parents were huddled next to the radio in a room with the curtains drawn. Dark, Wagner-like music was playing softly over the radio. My father was grim-faced, my mother tearful. Then my father said to me in a slow, low voice: 'My son, Dr Verwoerd was murdered today.'
>
> Tuesday was probably the closest Afrikanerdom came to that dark day 34 years ago.
>
> Hansie Cronjé was more than a sports hero. He was a symbol of what Afrikaners are capable of. He was a young man with a mooi oop gesig, a man who did not deny his relationship with his God, who respected his father, who was proud of his mother tongue, a young leader who did not laugh easily. He could walk tall in any city in the world, he met world leaders and looked them straight in the eye.

He was the national captain in a sport until recently dominated by the English. Hansie was Afrikanerdom's golden son.

Well, that is karma for you. FW de Klerk divorced his sweet wife for a Greek, Kallie Knoetze joined the African National Congress (ANC), Eugene Terre'Blanche is in jail, Pieter-Dirk Uys is a moffie, Tolla van der Merwe had a heart attack, Bles Bridges is dead.

The Bulls are at the bottom of the Super 12 log. The leader of the biggest Afrikaner political party, Tony Leon, is a Jew. En Hansie is 'n skelm, a crook. Caught by the Indians, nogal. Has God turned his back on his Chosen People?

I can see a PhD thesis in psychology already developing at Bloemfontein University: from match winner to match fixer – a study of temptations facing young Afrikaners. Or: is it really true that Afrikaners might be racists, but at least they are honest?

Yes, we still ask that question. We had our answer when Piet Retief tried to cheat Dingaan out of his land and cattle. We had our answer when some of the most prominent leaders of the volk were caught during the Info Scandal in the late 1970's.

We had our answer when deputy ministers Hennie van der Walt and Pietie du Plessis were thrown in jail for stealing. We had our answer when Magnus Malan lied to parliament about Anton Lubowski being an army spy. We had our answer when Adriaan Vlok swore on the Bible that the ANC blew up Khotso House. But we still ask the question.

I suddenly remember that the same dominee who reported to my parents that he was very worried about my moral fibre was caught in bed with the organ player the very next year. Really. He is now a respected and successful insurance salesman in my home town. God bless him.

But for a while, still, I think we will ask ourselves, how could Hansie have done it?

He was already a multimillionaire, he had an adoring nation at his feet, he was one of the most respected sportsmen internationally and he is an active Christian.

That is exactly it, I think. I think he was bored to his core with being so righteous and good and earnest. He was a good son to his parents, a good husband to his wife, a good deacon to his church, a good example to everybody's children.

He did not swear, smoke, drink, gamble or take drugs. The poor man needed desperately to sin in order to stay sane. As desperately as a good-looking woman of 30 who is still a virgin.

Or maybe Hansie was looking for excitement, looking for the rush that danger or recklessness so often brings. Like the filthy rich housewife who steals a R10 pair of panties from a super-market.

Or perhaps it was a case of you can take Hansie out of Bloemfontein, but you cannot take Bloemfontein out of Hansie.

As a native of Kroonstad I speak from experience here. Even when we have made it in the sophisticated world out there, we have this nagging little voice in our subconscious: if only they knew who I really am.

The only way to silence that little voice is to prove to yourself that you are as tough and as clever and as wise to the world as the next guy. Which means you sometimes also have to flirt with evil. If you think I am just a naïve, clean-faced boykie from Bloemfontein you are mistaken, pal. I can get down with the best and the worst of men.

Of course, it could have been greed pure and simple. There is serious competition among top sportsmen out there about material things.

Did you hear Francois got a million for that stupid ad? Did you hear Ernie is about to buy a ranch in Georgia? Have you seen Allan's new Porsche? Did you hear Hansie has just moved into his new place at Fancourt?

No, coming to think of it, I am sure it is the sin thing. It is the only way I will ever forgive him. But why did he not simply smoke a zol?

3

Players' perspectives

After interviewing Johan Volsteedt, I flew straight from Bloemfontein to Port Elizabeth for a meeting with 'the other favourite son', Kepler Wessels.

There were many reasons why it was important for me to get Wessels's views about the Hansie Cronjé affair. Firstly, there was the Grey College link between the two of them which, at the very least, seemed like an interesting angle. Furthermore, as the previous South African cricket captain, Wessels had been considered to be Cronjé's mentor over an extended period of time.

Added to this was the fact that Wessels's name had featured prominently during the proceedings of the King Commission, in the context of a supposed conversation between himself and Hansie Cronjé about an alleged match-fixing proposal during the Wills Triangular series in Pakistan in 1994. And finally, Wessels had earned himself a reputation as a straight talker – especially since his direct involvement with cricket ended, freeing him up to really speak his mind in regular press columns. Wasn't Wessels, after all, one of the first people to call for an independent investigation into match-fixing, refusing to discard the early rumours as 'rubbish'?

Kepler Wessels is quite an enigma in the world of South African sport. Widely regarded as one of the most talented cricketers that the country has ever produced, he never really attained the popularity that one would expect in the case of such a prodigious sports star. His contribution to the success of post-isolation cricket in South Africa is often underrated, with critics choosing to focus on a cramped style of batting rather than the man's unquestionable work ethic, competitive nature and leadership skills … not to mention his ability to score runs when it mattered most.

Even a 'love-him-or-hate-him' personality like Naas Botha always had more fans than enemies; this in spite of the fact that the height of Botha's playing career overlapped with an era of excessive provincialism, induced by deprivation from international competition in South Africa. Why did this same sports-loving public battle so much to warm to Kepler Wessels?

A lot of this, one has to say, was probably just sour grapes. Kepler managed to play proper test cricket in Australia whilst, back home, the closest most of his 'real' countrymen ever got to an international contest was fighting in a bush war. Then, a few years after he eventually returned home, Nelson Mandela was released from prison and the land of milk and honey at the tip of Africa opened up once more. At the end of 1991, a three-match tour to India was organised with Clive Rice as captain. But when Rice failed as a batsman, scoring a total of 26 for an average of 13 on tour, Wessels blossomed with an average of 70 and two Man of the Match awards. Within two ticks, Wessels was appointed as captain of the South African cricket team.

What a cheek! Talk about having your cake and eating it … and a lot of us didn't even think he was such a nice guy!

Bear in mind, however, that Kepler Wessels didn't appoint himself as national captain. He was simply approached to share his considerable experience with a bunch of hopeful cricketers who could play a bit but, frankly, only knew one another in the dog-eat-dog world of international sport. And if you're looking for nice guys, go to the beach; there was a job to get done here.

On the plane, I paged through the Kepler Wessels biography, written by Edward Griffiths. I witnessed how the author sings the ex-captain's praises. I read how Wessels carefully groomed the abundance of young South African talent in the early 1990s. Eventually, a specific paragraph caught my eye. Discussing the Kepler Wessels influence on Hansie Cronjé, an anecdote is relayed about the 1992 tour to the West Indies where Cronjé decided to cut his hair short just as Wessels had done:

> It was Tweedledum and Tweedledee to such an extent that other players began to resent Cronjé as a nodding puppy on the captain's lap.

Funny that; I wondered how many times Cronjé had ever been described as a nodding puppy in anyone's lap.

As I walked into the office of Kepler Wessels, my first reaction was one of mild shock. Somehow one doesn't expect a top sportsman ever to settle down to something as mundane as a suit and tie. But this was Kepler Wessels the businessman. He made it clear to me that he was no longer involved in any form of cricket whatsoever, with the exception of writing his column. I apologised for my own casual attire and got a smile in return. So he does smile, does he?

When I conveyed greetings from Volsteedt, Kepler followed up with another lighthearted moment. 'Did he tell you about Steve Hofmeyr's phone call?' Steve Hofmeyr is an Afrikaans pop star who had also been to Grey College.

'Apparently Steve asked Mr Volsteedt what was going on at the school. First there was Kepler Wessels who had a reputation for being obstreperous, then there was Steve Hofmeyr with a reputation for being a womaniser and now there was Hansie Cronjé with a reputation for you know what.' Now I can certainly vouch for it, Kepler does smile.

We got down to the serious business. Interestingly, Kepler Wessels doesn't see himself as such a big mentor to Hansie Cronjé. Yes, they've known each other from a young age (Hansie's mother was Kepler's tennis coach as far back as nursery school days in Bloemfontein), but the twelve-year age gap between Wessels and Cronjé meant that they were never really close. And when they eventually ended up playing cricket together for South Africa, it was for a comparatively short period.

Kepler's first memories of Hansie as a cricketer date back to the 1987-1988 season, when Wessels captained Eastern Province and Cronjé made his debut for Free State as a schoolboy. Four years later, Cronjé joined the short tour to India as a development player. Wessels recalled how it was Cronjé's disciplined approach to fitness and a determination to fight to the bitter end that impressed him most in those early days. These were, after all, traits that the two of them shared.

'It was clear from the beginning that Hansie would one day take over from me,' Kepler told me. 'Yes, when I eventually stopped playing for South Africa the captaincy was theoretically a toss-up between Jonty Rhodes and Cronjé, but I don't think there was ever much doubt that Hansie would get it.' I was reminded of how Johan Volsteedt had told me earlier in the day that Jonty Rhodes was pipped to the position of captaincy by Cronjé once before: when they played together for South African Schools in 1987.

'In my last couple of years as captain, Hansie was my vice-captain. He was, in fact, always meant to take over from me earlier than he eventually did. I wanted to retire straight after our tour of England; I mean there's no better way to end an international cricket career than the test century I managed to score at Lord's. And I had, in fact, informed the UCBSA of my intentions at the beginning of that year. But Hansie had such a bad tour – I think he averaged about 17 or 18 – that his confidence seemed really low. Eventually, the selectors begged me to stay on for the limited-overs series in Pakistan a month later.'

'How was Hansie as vice-captain?' I asked.

'Well, initially he did the job just fine. But later on, I didn't really have much support from him ... in fact, maybe I trusted him too much at one point,' was Kepler's response.

'What do you mean by trusting him too much?' I wondered.

'Well, let me put it to you this way. The vice-captain's job is largely to share the captain's load; to try and take some of the pressure off him. But it's not easy to do that if you're battling so much with your own form. Hansie ended up a total introvert during the latter stages of that English tour. It was when I realised this, that I started relying less on him.

'After I stopped playing for South Africa, the two of us slowly started drifting apart,' Wessels continued. 'We never played together again, and I took on some media responsibilities. The nature of the job when you write for newspapers is simply such that there will be times when you have to question some of the decisions made by the national captain – this is true in spite of the fact that Hansie and I probably agreed on 90% of tactical issues.

'So, no, I wouldn't describe our friendship as a particularly close one. But it's not a terrible one either. And there was no defining moment in the way that it developed; it was more of a natural evolutionary process.' Cordial, I thought, is what one calls such a relationship.

Did Kepler have any regrets? 'Well ... not really,' was his response, shrugging his shoulders. 'But when I now look at all these things that have happened, maybe I should have stuck it out a little longer with the national team. The guys were very young and relatively inexperienced, you know ...'

So, what's Kepler's opinion? Why did 'these things' happen?

'We'll probably never really know. But I do think Hansie had quite a lot of control in the end. It was evident that Bob Woolmer's influence started dissipating after his first couple of years as a coach, once he started having less to offer the team.'

'Tell me, Kepler,' I asked just before leaving, 'what exactly happened at the governmental reception that Hansie referred to in his testimony before the King Commission?'

'You mean the match-fixing story with the Australians? Now that's a good question – it's about time that I get a chance to clear that one up.' Thanks, I thought – at least now I knew how Mr Wessels felt about the rest of my questions. But then again, that's exactly why I wanted to speak to the man, because I knew that he wouldn't be afraid to call a spade a spade.

'There was never such an incident at any reception I attended. What did happen, was that I had a drink with a few of the Australians in their team room one evening in 1994. They told me in passing about some approach that had been made relating to possible match-fixing. The next morning, I told Peter Pollock about this over breakfast. But to be frank, between the two of us we didn't even think it was much of an issue. A few months later, the accusations made by Tim May and Shane Warne relating to an approach by Salim Malik became public knowledge. But I never discussed this with Hansie.'

Now I was puzzled. I grabbed my file with preparatory notes, searching fervently for a specific quote from the King Commission. I ripped the page out and read Hansie's words out to Kepler: '... at some stage, Kepler Wessels had told me that he was part of – not part of, he was sitting at the same table when this apparent approach must have been made ...'

'Nope,' Kepler insisted, 'it never happened.'

'So why did Hansie say this?' I wondered.

'Dunno; I can only hope that he made an honest mistake.'

I checked the transcripts of the King Commission again. Hansie Cronjé also referred to a one-day international against Pakistan in Faisalabad in 1994, saying that 'the team was joking about the fact that we thought that they had been throwing the game'.

'Do you remember that game, Kepler – wasn't it your last game for

83

South Africa?'

'Ja, it was, and I still scored a fifty that day which was nice to end off with. We batted first and posted a score of 220 odd. We quickly had Pakistan 76 for 4 or something, at which point Hansie came to me with a huge smile on his face. He remarked that if we ended up winning that match, people would really think that it had been fixed. To this day, I don't know why he ever said that. I don't remember the team joking about it, but I do remember that comment ...'

As we said good-bye to each other, Kepler had a final message. 'Let me make one point very clear to you: in the more than twenty years that I played representative cricket, I was not approached once by any bookmakers or match-fixers or anybody of the sort.'

With the meeting over, Kepler had to rush off. I went to his father's place – Kepler thought he might have some photographs that I could borrow. I ended up spending a couple of hours with a proud Mr Wessels Senior. Although I didn't get any photographs, I did find out that Kepler has turned into a mean bowls player. Don't say I didn't warn you if he soon represents his country again. No half measures in the case of Kepler Wessels: he only plays to win.

On the plane back to Cape Town that night, I paged through his biography again. Now that I'd met Kepler, the description of his personality was of even more interest than before:

> ... it never stops. The incessant droning about how he never lightens up (he does), about how he never grins (he does, often), about how he is just too deadly dour (he isn't).

I could only chuckle in agreement as I slowly drifted to sleep. It had been quite a day.

*　*　*　*　*

The next player on my list of people to speak to was Craig Matthews. Whereas Hansie Cronjé had been vice-captain to Kepler Wessels, Matthews in turn was vice-captain to Cronjé, until a rude end to his international career in January 1997 occurred when he sprained an ankle delivering his first ball, in a one-day international against Zimbabwe. The ball went to the boundary and Matthews went to the hospital – never to play for his country again.

Craig Matthews has been one of the most enduring names in South African cricket in recent history. He made his debut for Western Province in the 1987/88 season and first played for the national team during the tour to India upon South Africa's re-admission to international cricket in November 1991. A natural leader, he captained his province for many years in addition to being vice-captain for his country.

I remember meeting Matthews for the first time a few days after he tried to hold on to a catching chance off his own bowling, offered by Lance Klusener in a day-night provincial match at the end of 1999. In typical Zulu fashion the ball had not been struck gently and the bowler's thumb was split open. I was told it was even more painful than it looked. Having had enough bad luck for one career, Matthews decided to retire from competitive cricket at the ripe old age of 35 a few months later. He does, however, maintain strong links with the game, and the only province he knows, as Marketing Manager of Western Province Cricket.

Craig Matthews and Hansie Cronjé go back a long way. Although Matthews is a little bit older, their careers started in the same seaon and over the next twelve years they would end up playing a lot of cricket together for their country, as well as against each other as opposing provincial captains. Based on this, it is not altogether unexpected that they would retain a friendship after cricket.

'Yes, we're still good mates,' Matthews said when we met. 'It's not like we're closest buddies or anything like that, but we still chat quite often. And I don't actually think that he has too many close friends. You must remember, people like Hansie don't have as much opportunity to make friends as "normal people" do. When somebody like yourself was probably buggering around with mates at varsity in your early twenties, Hansie was either putting in some extra practice session, or he was touring some remote part of the continent where there's only horrible food, or he had to keep a straight face in front of reporters at a post-match press conference.

'So someone like Hansie ends up mixing socially with only a handful of people over a period of ten or fifteen years – at exactly the time when most people cement their most enduring relationships. The public should therefore also not think it strange that he became friendly with someone like Mohammed Azharruddin. The two of them probably saw more of each other than Hansie saw of his parents in a typical year. You can probably compare the captain of a national sports team with the beauty queen who never gets a decent boyfriend: half the guys are intimidated by her looks and her status, and the other half are of the type that she may not want to mix with in the first place.'

Point taken. The bottom line is, Craig Matthews still has a lot of loyalty to Hansie Cronjé. In fact, they were scheduled to play golf together at Fancourt three days after my interview with Craig. In spite of this, Matthews didn't have a problem chatting to me. 'Things have happened, you know, you can't deny it. But life goes on, and times like these are what friends are for, not so?' he remarked philosophically when we originally set up the appointment.

Matthews elaborated. 'We were also quite similar in many ways, specifically as far as our respect for the game was concerned. And on the field we would be equally serious, didn't matter how much fun we could get up to afterwards. Although, of course, Hansie had a lot more talent than I ever had.'

To underline the strength of their relationship, Craig proudly told me about a series of paintings that Hansie had commissioned as part of his benefit year in 1997. The originals were auctioned off at the time, but limited-edition copies of some of them could still be bought. There was a specific one, the theme of which was something like 'People that had played an important part in Hansie's life'. And the three people in this picture, in addition to Hansie himself, were Craig Matthews, Jonty Rhodes and Nelson Mandela.

I asked Craig how he felt when the reports about Hansie's alleged phone transcripts first came out. 'I guess my reaction was a form of denial at first,' he said, 'but I just hoped it wasn't true.'

'You realise, of course, that *hoping* it wasn't true, also means you concede it *might* actually have been true?'

'I guess that's fair comment,' he said, nodding his head, 'so now you probably want to know why I thought that?' It was my turn to nod my head.

'Look, Hansie has now spoken openly about his love of money. So I can probably also talk about it … it's been quite obvious to some of us over a long period of time.'

'Why do you say that?' I teased. 'Is it because he never bought you a drink, like he said at the King Commission?'

'No, that's crap, of course he's bought me a drink. I don't know why he ever said that. But he was always extremely conscious of what things were worth. I remember once, it was just after the New Year's test against England at Newlands in 1996. I think we beat the Poms by ten wickets inside three days – probably because I didn't play that game,' he chuckled, 'so we had some time off as a squad. I had a mate who had a yacht at the Water Club in Granger Bay and he invited a few of us around on a cruise. I still remember, it was just before the Cape to Rio race. And you could see Hansie was just fascinated by this boat. He basically didn't stop asking about what it was worth, what it cost to maintain and so on. And also what somebody had to be worth in order to afford that kind of luxury. That was always quite a big thing to him: what people were worth. Was R10 million a lot of money? Or did one actually need R50 million to be *really* rich?'

'Wait a minute,' I interrupted him, 'that's the kind of speculation that a lot of my friends and colleagues would often keep themselves busy with. Do you really think it's such a big deal?'

'Well, in the case of investment people it may be different. I guess you guys work with money all the time, so maybe it's not so funny in your case. But I can tell you, that's not the kind of conversation that cricketers typically have. Anyway, there were other examples as well. Hansie was always very knowledgeable about shares and stuff. And he would seldom go to a smart restaurant. He simply didn't see the value in spending a lot of money on an expensive meal if a pizza would fill you up just as well. He was just always conscious of amounts and prices and values. That's why the story that he didn't know how many dollars he had in the cupboard, when he had to phone Bertha to count it, has never made sense to me.'

Craig continued. 'It wasn't just the money either; I think it had a lot to do with status. Hansie was always very conscious of celebrities. I remember once, with the launch of the SABC's new channels a few years ago, the cricket team was invited. Hansie walked across to Johnny Cochran (O.J. Simpson's lawyer) and asked for his autograph. Another time, when we were in New Zealand, we bumped into Cheryl Ladd and he got her autograph as well.'

I asked Craig how he thought the whole affair had started. 'I honestly think it might have just started as a joke. He was a bit of a maverick; he sometimes had a funny sense of humour. He would often test you, just to see what your reaction was, and then, depending on your own response, he would sometimes act in a way you'd never have expected.

'For example, when I was his vice-captain, there would be times on the field where the situation demanded that Allan Donald be given a bowling spell. We needed a breakthrough, we may have known that the batsman wasn't too comfortable against fast bowling, Allan was fresh, et cetera. Hansie would then walk up to me and say, "Hey, don't you think I should have a bowl?" And what he's doing is, he's just teasing me, so if I said, "Don't be stupid, Allan should bowl," that's exactly what would happen. But if I said, "Sure, why not," he might actually have a go himself, even though the situation determined otherwise. So I can see that he might have got pulled in like that. What started as a bit of a tease, ended as a tragedy.'

This theory of Matthews fits in well with Hansie Cronjé's own testimony before the King Commission. At one point, Cronjé described the way that he interacted with his players, referring to ' ... my way of showing a little bit of my naughty side to them ... '. On another occasion, Shamila Batohi, the leader of the evidence on behalf of the commission, asked Cronjé what he would have done assuming Pat Symcox was supportive of the first offer ever made to Cronjé (at the time of the Mandela Cup, January 1995). Hansie Cronjé responded as follows: 'It is very hard to say, we probably would have gone through with it ... '

Craig Matthews also spoke about the impact the affair would have on the support for the game. 'I think the saddest part is the kids. Let me tell you about my nephews. They often play cricket in their back yard with their mom, and you know the way kids are: when they play, they're not Chad and Drew, they're Allan Donald and Jonty Rhodes. Their mother tells me she went into bat the other day and was obviously asked to identify herself. "Oh, I'll be Craig Matthews," she said. "Don't be silly, Craig can't bat," came back the response. "OK, I'll be Hansie Cronjé," she tried again. "No you can't, Hansie is a cheat," she was overruled again.'

But Craig Matthews feels sorry for Hansie himself, too. 'I honestly think he's already paid a much heavier price than he actually deserves. Who else has ever been interrogated like that on national television? But

I think the worst part for him is simply to wake up in the mornings and to realise that he will never again be able to have anything to do with cricket, the game that he'd lived for, for such a long time; the one thing which he could really do better than most other people in the world. Do you have an idea what it feels like when that's taken away from you – even if you only have yourself to blame?'

'And Herschelle Gibbs? You've also known him for a long time, not so?'

Craig smiled and shook his head. 'Shame man, you can't really blame him for anything. I was actually his first captain in senior cricket. I still remember his first game for Province, against Northern Transvaal at the beginning of 1991. We were in Pretoria and the team went out one evening; most of the guys would have ordered a beer. And there was Herschelle, just a kid of 16, asking for a bubblegum milk shake.'

As he was telling the story, Craig didn't once stop shaking his head. He went on. 'What do you expect from someone like Herschelle? He's probably the most talented player in the team, but cricket is the only thing he knows, and he's the kind of guy that really looks up to a mentor. I think I played that role for a long time, that's why I actually wrote a letter on his behalf for purposes of the UCBSA's disciplinary hearing. But obviously Hansie would have taken over where I left off in the last few years. So ja, I think it's quite understandable that the captain could draw him into something if he wanted to.'

Speaking about the influence Hansie Cronjé had on other people, Craig told me a story that he'd heard on a talk radio station, just as news of the match-fixing scandal first broke. Somebody phoned in and said that he couldn't identify himself as he was a professional psychologist, but he'd been involved in a team-building exercise with members of the South African cricket team in the past. He also stressed that he'd worked with lots of companies and highly rated professionals from the business world in his time. In his professional assessment, however, this psychologist had never come across a personality as strong as Hansie Cronjé's, or someone with the ability to manipulate other people like the ex-captain of the Proteas could.

At the King Commission, Jacques Kallis was the one player who emphasised Hansie's strong personality in particular, describing it as follows. 'He's strong in his beliefs, and he just came across as a person who really backed himself, and never sort of stood down to anyone.'

In closing, I asked Craig Matthews a general question. 'So where do you think all this match-fixing stuff will end?'

Craig collected his thoughts. 'I don't know, but I honestly think it's time the authorities cleared matters up, once and for all. I mean cricket is my business, it's my life, I don't want to keep on reading all this stuff in the newspapers either.'

As we both got up to go back to work, Craig asked me if I wanted him to arrange a meeting with Hansie Cronjé himself, as he was scheduled to play golf with Hansie a few days later.

'Yeah, why not,' I said. 'I have, after all, already tried to get hold of him myself.'

But unfortunately that never materialised.

*   *   *   *   *

You'll go far to find two people more different than Richard Snell and Hansie Cronjé. Hansie is an Afrikaner from Bloemfontein, Richard is an Englishman from Durban – the last outpost of the British Empire. Hansie has always been a very focused individual; Richard is pretty laid-back. Everyone knows that Hansie was mature way ahead of his time; Richard's boyish charm is still a trademark feature.

But they could both play a bit of cricket. A bowler on the fast side of fast-medium, Snellie, as Richard is generally known, had the rare ability to swing the ball both ways. And when he opened his shoulders, he could also hit it further than most.

In spite of all the differences between the two of them, you can tell that Richard Snell and Hansie Cronjé have always had a very good relationship. More importantly, Snellie still has a lot of respect for his ex-captain.

Richard and Hansie's relationship goes back even further than the one between Craig Matthews and Hansie. The fact that Snell and Cronjé matriculated in the same year, meant that they had two years together in the South African Schools' side. Over the nine years that followed, they would end up playing a lot of cricket together for their country.

Snellie started reminiscing. 'I still remember when Hansie captained SA Schools in 1987. He was just so far ahead of everyone else when it came to his approach to the game and the way that he thought about it.

You could just tell that he'd read every cricket book at a young age. Not only that, but he also had an amazing ability to remember the stuff. You could always walk up to him and ask, "Remind me how we got this bloke out last time" – and he'd give you a rundown of dismissals.'

Hansie Cronjé gave an example of this memory for cricket detail at the King Commission. In response to a question about South Africa's fall of wickets in a test against India in December 1996, he responded as follows. 'Without looking at the record, I would think and I want to test myself, Ms Batohi. Andrew Hudson and myself were batting together, I think the score was about 30 or 40 and we put on about 60 or 70 and then there was a reasonable collapse after that. I think Lance Klusener got 30 odd not out, I think he was the only other batsman to get a reasonable score, but I will check … ' The actual scorecard for the match showed that Hansie Cronjé joined Andrew Hudson with the score on 39 for 3, they had a partnership of 58 runs, and Lance Klusener made 34 not out. Not bad at all.

Snellie continued. 'I'll always remember Hansie as a hell of a nice guy. But he was no pushover. I'll never forget our game after the 1987 Nuffield Week which was held in Bloemfontein. There is a tradition that the SA Schools team plays against the local provincial side, so we were pitched against Free State just at the time that they were becoming a force in South African cricket. Guys like AD (Allan Donald) were established members of their team by that time, and of course AD was already a lot faster than probably any schoolboy bowler in the world. But Hansie knew AD because they'd basically grown up together, and he was certainly not intimidated in the slightest. He scored a hundred that day, and on a few occasions – with the ball on its way to the boundary – AD gave him That Famous Stare. And Hansie would return the compliment by staring right back, not intimidated in the least by the person who would become South Africa's main strike bowler over the next ten years.'

Richard took a mental leap forward and started talking about their international career. 'I'll never forget that test in Sydney at the beginning of 1994 when Kepler injured himself and Hansie took over as captain for the first time. I was twelfth man, and I was sitting next to Kepler as the drama unfolded on the last day. It was uncanny, but basically every time that Kepler thought the field placing should change or someone else should have a bowl, Hansie would do exactly that within less than an over. He just knew the game from the very beginning.'

Richard Snell was always known as one of the fastest members of the South African cricket team, but if there was ever anybody who could give him a run for his money, it was Hansie Cronjé. 'He could run five kilometres in fifteen minutes; not many people can do that. I think he used to train with Zola Budd when both of them were still in Bloemfontein. And as far as I know, Hansie still has outstanding bets with a few people that he will one day get a gold medal in the Comrades Marathon.'

Snellie also told me about the Super Sportsman competition in which both he and Hansie participated, in 1993. The competition was won by Daley Thompson, two-times Olympic champion and world recordholder in the decathlon. Widely considered to be one of the most versatile sportsmen ever, Thompson never lost in competition over a nine-year period during the 80s. But Hansie Cronjé gave him a good go on the day, and he actually beat Thompson in a number of the events.

To summarise, Richard Snell had nothing but good things to say about Hansie Cronjé. 'It's just a sad, sad story …'

* * * * *

Having discussed Hansie Cronjé's phenomenal commitment to fitness with people like Kepler Wessels and Richard Snell, it was interesting also to get a perspective from Craig Smith, the physiotherapist of the South African cricket team. Craig is in the unique position to have been connected with every match, every tour and every single day's cricket in which the Proteas have been involved, since re-admission to international cricket in November 1991. No player, coach or administrator can say this. In fact, the closest anyone else has ever come to this statistic is Hansie Cronjé himself, having been marginally more involved than people such as Jonty Rhodes and Allan Donald over this period.

Having 'seen 'em all', it was indeed telling when Craig Smith confirmed that Hansie Cronjé was, by quite a long way, the fittest and most hard-working player with whom he had ever dealt. Of equal significance was the fact that this remained true over the full eight years of Hansie's involvement with the team. It applied to Cronjé 'the youngster', when his dedication was rivalled only by Kepler Wessels, the

'… and nothing but the truth'?

two of them regularly putting in additional training sessions together on days off. It also applied to Cronjé 'the elder', when he would always lead from the front as captain, often putting some of the more junior members of the squad to shame in the process.

Smith also confirmed Hansie's talents as a runner. He told me that Cronjé ran the Two Oceans as a junior. Afterwards, I would confirm that Hansie Cronjé did in fact participate in the 56-kilometre ultra-marathon as an eighteen-year-old, on the 2nd of April 1988. He was the 11th youngest athlete in the race, out of a total of 7,000 entries. Finishing in 4 hours and 50 minutes, he beat more than 75% of the field and was the third junior home.

After years of rigorous training, Hansie Cronjé's knee eventually gave in after the 1997-1998 tour of Australia, and he had to undergo an operation for cartilage wear and tear. Up to that point, Cronjé had hardly ever been injured. Craig Smith thought that Hansie may have viewed being treated as a weakness, and often would prefer to train through a niggle or slight injury. In fact, in Smith's opinion, Cronjé would actually draw on the discomfort and turn it into a motivating factor. It was evident of his attitude that if he was hurting a bit, it was considered to be a good sign – a sign that he was training hard – and being able to get through it and overcome the injury on his own, was a sign of strength to himself.

Smith refers to this jokingly as '... a Bloemfontein mentality – I mean, what else is there to do in a place like that?', he said, a slight grin to be found on his otherwise sphinx-like face. 'I honestly thing the Grey College sportsmen achieve so much because there is less distraction for the boys up there, so all afternoon and on weekends they spend their time playing or training or practising whereas boys like myself from Cape Town spend our time on the beach or surfing or taking in the beautiful surroundings.'

Craig shared with me how Hansie sometimes became visibly frustrated with some of the people who had more raw cricket talent than himself, if they didn't want to match him in training; people like Daryll Cullinan, Allan Donald, Jacques Kallis, Herschelle Gibbs and Lance Klusener. In fact, I was astounded to hear from Craig that Klusener never did a full net practice (facing up to bowlers at full speed); the all-rounder would only do a limited number of throw-downs with the coach, before going in to face up to the world's quickest and best bowlers.

We turned to Hansie's involvement with bookmakers. In spite of Craig

Smith's tremendous respect for Hansie Cronjé, the leader and the athlete, Smith was visibly dismayed by the incident. 'I think what upset me most was that he always drove everyone else so hard, to train, to perform, to achieve. But then he's the one that takes money on the side, and we hear about it afterwards.' It's a bit like a manager of a company abusing cheap labour in order to enrich himself, I thought.

I asked Craig about some of the quotes that had been ascribed to him in the press since the betting scandal broke. 'Yeah', he responded, 'I did say it felt like there was pressure for Henry Williams to play in that final game in Nagpur, but there was never any *direct* pressure – I mean Hansie never came and said "he has to play or else!"'

'I also said it was strange that Hansie should have this free phone and all the free calls,' Smith continued. 'The manager and the coach and sometimes myself get phones to do our jobs, but not in the case of the Indian tour – and then Hansie had this phone. But I suppose that's just how it happened; he could have had his own contact.

'I was actually not that surprised about the news in the end,' Craig concluded. 'It was always quite evident how important money was to Hansie. I mean, we could all do with more money, but one shouldn't be obsessed with it ...'

* * * * *

It is interesting to note how the anecdotal evidence that one picks up when chatting to some of the ex-players relates to what was said in testimony before the King Commission.

Without exception, all the players that appeared before the commission confirmed they had the utmost respect for Hansie Cronjé; many of them referred to him as probably the best captain South Africa ever had.

Yes, a lot of them were shocked when the captain of the national side first approached them with a match-fixing proposal in India at the end of 1996. But not all of them. Daryll Cullinan referred to it as 'a stroke of genius', believing that Hansie Cronjé merely did it to motivate a team that was low on morale at the time.

And most of the players referred to his sense of humour at some point during their testimony. The way that Herschelle Gibbs summed it up was typical of a number of people's testimony, ' ... that is the thing with Hansie ... you just never know when he is being serious ... ' This certainly confirmed what Craig Matthews had said about the way that Cronjé would often tease people. And Derek Crookes pointed out how Hansie Cronjé '... often speaks in the same tone, whether he is joking or being serious'.

Despite the high regard that most of the players still appeared to have for their ex-captain, it would appear that a lot of them didn't have particularly close relationships with Hansie. Daryll Cullinan explained how he'd tried to contact Cronjé, unsuccessfully. 'I just wished to express sentiments of "I am thinking of you and the very best of luck and what must happen, must happen", along those sort of lines. I think that is a normal procedure for anyone who spent eight years in your career together.'

Henry Williams also testified that he'd had no contact with Cronjé whatsoever; subsequent press reports referred to a degree of bitterness in this regard. According to testimony before the commission, Cronjé did send messages to Williams, via Herschelle Gibbs, at the time that the story first broke. In Williams's own words, ' ... through Herschelle Gibbs, Cronjé said we must not tell the truth.'

According to Pieter Strydom's testimony, he did get a phone call from Hansie Cronjé not long after news of the scandal first broke, just to find out how he was. Strydom continued to say that he told Hansie he couldn't lie to the commission, to which Cronjé replied, 'It's fine. You can tell exactly what happened, but just don't mention the money.'

Interestingly, the one current player who seemed to remain closest to Hansie Cronjé through all the turmoil (except perhaps for Nicky Bojé who practically grew up with Cronjé), was the one who arguably had the most to lose in the process, namely Herschelle Gibbs. Not only would most people agree that Herschelle is more talented than most (and, by definition, he therefore has more to lose than anyone else), but he is also a lot younger than people like Henry Williams and Pieter Strydom (and therefore has a much longer cricket career ahead of him which has been endangered). Yet, in spite of what had happened, Gibbs described his relationship with Cronjé as follows: ' ... I've become really close to him and I think he's ... one of the few guys in the team that I can only say is my friend.' Soon after the first round of the King Commission's hearings had come to an end, there was further evidence of this when it was reported that Herschelle Gibbs had achieved a hole-in-one at Sparrebosch, the new ultra-luxurious golf development on the Knysna Heads. His partner on the day? Hansie Cronjé.

The extent to which Gibbs had trusted Cronjé was illustrated by his response to a question about why Hansie Cronjé should be asking Herschelle ' ... to deceive the Cricket Board and deceive the world ... '. Herschelle Gibbs replied by saying, 'I don't know why he asked me, but I was happy to go along with whatever he asked me to.'

Nicky Bojé told the King Commission not only about his friendship with Cronjé, but also how close their parents remain. Bojé stressed that he supported Cronjé and that he'd forgiven Cronjé for implicating Bojé himself. Both Cronjé and Bojé insisted in their evidence before the commission that Cronjé had never actually approached Bojé in the context of any match-fixing.

* * * * *

While researching this book, the following incident was relayed to me:

'But there are so many stories now. Steve Waugh told us about quite an interesting incident the other day. Australia was playing Pakistan in Hobart at the beginning of 1997. Apparently it had been raining for about three days before the match. On the morning of the game, however, the sun came out and you could practically hear the grass grow under the covers – this was like fast bowlers' paradise. As Mark Taylor and Wasim Akram walked down for the toss, Taylor found out that Waqar Younis, who was pretty much the fastest bowler in the world at the time, would be "rested" and two of the specialist spinners were playing instead. Taylor could hardly hide his amazement, but worse was to follow. Pakistan won the toss and elected to bat. Now in those kind of conditions, most captains would bowl 19 times out of 20. And the twentieth time, they would think a little bit and then they would also bowl. So of course Pakistan was never going to post a high score; I think they were bowled out for under 150. In response, however, Australia had a batting collapse like you've seldom seen from them.

'And the more wickets fell, the less excited most of the Pakistan players seemed to be – you can figure out for yourself why. Apparently

Wasim Akram called the team together at one point when Australia lost their sixth wicket with the score on about 100. At this point it had become quite clear that Pakistan were now favourites to win the match. Akram had to urge the players to look a little bit happier when the next wicket fell. Aamer Sohail is probably the one who told Steve Waugh about this – remember, he was the one who was eventually banned from Pakistani cricket after blowing the whistle on some of his team-mates' betting activities.'

* * * * *

Whichever way you look at it, Hansie Cronjé touched the lives of those who played the game with him. And when you speak to some of them, and you read the evidence that others gave to the King Commission, you can only shake your head in disbelief at what had happened.

In Hansie Cronjé's own words, a lot of his dealings with bookmakers boiled down to merely 'stringing them along'. What's hard to believe, however, is that Cronjé managed to do the same to his team-mates – the very people that lived closest to him over the last few years.

4

Others who know Hansie

It was never going to be easy to chat about the affair to anyone who knows Hansie Cronjé well. Firstly, the matter was sub judice at the time that this book was being written. Any 'insiders' I approached would thus be hesitant to talk without their lawyers present. Secondly, even if there were no specific legal issues, there were still tremendous sensitivities due to people's positions, as well as their relationships with Hansie.

I was fortunate in that a good friend of mine knew people well, like the incumbent national coach, Graham Ford. Fordie, as he likes to be called, was therefore the first person I approached when researching this book. His immediate response was that he would be more than happy to chat to me, as long as I had the go-ahead from Hansie. When I explained to him that I had indeed approached Cronjé, and that I was still waiting for him to come back to me – and after convincing him that I wasn't searching for sensation – he eventually agreed to see me.

Fordie is not a man of many words. The quintessential nice guy, he prefers to let the results of his teams do the talking. As a sports administrator at the University of Natal in Pietermaritzburg during the late 80s, he quickly proceeded from the position of player-coach of the university team, to coaching the Natal Colts under-23 team. It was during this time that he worked with an abundance of talent in players such as Jonty Rhodes, Shaun Pollock, Lance Klusener, Dale Benkenstein and Neil Johnson (who would go on to open both batting and bowling for Zimbabwe) to name but a few.

When many of these players graduated to the Natal senior team and

Mike Procter moved on to greener pastures by accepting a coaching position in English county cricket, it was perhaps natural that the players would have their say in having Fordie appointed as Natal coach in 1992. Seven years later, and with a lot of these same players now in the South African side, the process effectively repeated itself. Fordie was appointed national coach in Bob Woolmer's place. Thus it came to be that someone who had never played cricket at the highest level, was put in charge of one of the greatest powers in the international game.

Given his personality, it should not come as any surprise that Fordie had nothing negative to say about the national captain with whom he had worked for just one year. Of course, he and the players were deeply disappointed about what had transpired – some even angry. But in the end, there was no getting away from the fact that Hansie was someone who had been a friend to most of them; someone with whom they had gone into battle, someone who had left his mark on each and every one of them. And you don't just forget all of that overnight.

On Tuesday the 11th of April 2000, the day that Hansie made his first confession, the national team was in Durban for the first of three one-day internationals against Australia, which was to take place at Kingsmead the following day. A crisis meeting was called by Fordie and everybody was given the chance to speak their mind. The meeting did not end until there was consensus that the air had been cleared amongst all the members of the team. The team then agreed that – as far as they were concerned – that would be the end of the matter; none of them wanted to talk about it again. They would not allow the controversy to dominate the task at hand which was simply 'to beat the hell out of the Aussies'. (It would only come out much later that Herschelle Gibbs wasn't quite truthful at the time.)

The strategy seemed to work. At the start of the match at Kingsmead the next day, the team did a lap around the field and a large crowd (especially considering the relatively early start on a normal working day) gave them a standing ovation. This gave the team a tremendous lift, and after that it was always going to be a difficult day for Australia. The rest is history. Not only did South Africa beat the Aussies by 6 wickets on the day, with Makhaya Ntini returning his best bowling figures ever, and Man of the Match, Gary Kirsten, scoring a near century, they also wrapped up the three-match series 2-1 a few days later.

According to Fordie, he – like most of us – never believed that Hansie had done anything wrong until the 11 April confession. This may seem strange, he admitted, given the close relationship that a coach and captain are expected to have with one another. But then again, there were a number of mitigating circumstances.

Neither Hansie nor Fordie has a particularly outgoing personality. Yes, Hansie has an exceptionally strong personality, but he is mostly a very private individual. Put two people like that together and you shouldn't expect either to bare his soul in a hurry. Hansie was often the loner, having meals by himself and spending time alone in his hotel room. And the shy Fordie would never force himself into anyone else's space, preferring rather to build up a solid friendship slowly. Fordie also did not share any of the history with Hansie that he does with a number of the Natal players in the squad.

One could argue that Bob Woolmer would have had a better chance to know about Hansie's dealings with the bookies, given that they had had a relationship over a much longer period of time. It is significant to note, however, how much praise Bob has heaped on Cronjé in his autobiography *Woolmer on Cricket*. Timing of the book's publication could hardly have been more ironic: it was in the final stages of the publishing process just as news of the Cronjé betting scandal broke.

Yes, Woolmer does point out that Hansie 'was seen as the epitome of the unsmiling Afrikaaner (sic)'. He also writes about Cronjé's 'moods, tantrums and troubled states of mind', saying that 'Hansie's face is like a book: when he is cross, he has very frightening facial features ... he smoulders ... he used to roar in torrents'.

To top it all, it is clear that the coach's relationship with his captain did not end on a perfect note, as Woolmer begins his book by describing his departure from South African cricket and the active role that Cronjé played in the matter. Woolmer also states openly that there were times when he thought he could not trust Cronjé.

But the negatives about Hansie are far outnumbered by the positives in Woolmer's book. He compliments Cronjé's fitness and describes him as a dedicated, determined and passionate team man. He calls Cronjé one of the best captains South Africa has ever had or will ever have. Woolmer also describes how even Brian Lara acknowledged Cronjé's superior leadership skills during the West Indies' catastrophic tour in

1998/99, when he approached the South African captain to learn how to get the team to play together.

When Bob Woolmer jetted into South Africa to market the biography, the hype around the betting scandal was at its peak, and the King Commission was about to begin proceedings. At that point, Woolmer had a few more critical things to say about Hansie Cronjé than he had volunteered in the book. He was quoted, for example, as saying that Cronjé had had too much control, and that the ex-captain only once apologised to him – after being pressurised to do so. But the coach kept insisting that he did not believe that any matches in the Woolmer-Cronjé regime had ever been thrown.

One of the most telling paragraphs in Woolmer's book – given the timing of its publication – is the famous monograph by Lord Harris which he quotes towards the end of the book:

> You do well to love Cricket, for it is more free from anything sordid, anything dishonourable, than any game in the world. To play it keenly, generously, self-sufficiently, is a moral lesson in itself, and the classroom is God's air and sunshine. Foster it my brothers, so that it may attract all who find the time to play it, and protect it from anything that may try and sully it so that it may grow in favour with all men and women.

Ironic? Yes. But it probably also proves that the departing coach really had no idea about some of the dealings which may have been going on around him.

Fordie remembered that there were often people who came and saw Cronjé, but hastened to add that there were people who came and saw every other member of the squad as well. 'Surely everybody's entitled to friends,' he said, 'and the life of a cricketer is tough enough, very often being away from your family for months on end.' He had therefore never asked questions about to whom his players had spoken. The members of the team were, after all, grown-up men.

There was also the simple issue of trust. Just like a marriage, characterised by a husband and wife spying on each other, would ultimately be doomed to fail, so too would a relationship between coach and captain, not built on absolute trust, never work. There were many

'... and nothing but the truth'?

examples of this. Often tough decisions needed to be implemented. Leaving out a senior player from the team when he was battling with form, disciplining somebody whose behaviour may have been found wanting; there would be chaos if the coach and the captain did not speak as one.

Moreover, according to Fordie, there was simply no reason not to trust Hansie. Here was a player with a proven track record and someone with unquestionable integrity …

Graham Ford was full of praise for Hansie Cronjé, and stressed that the two of them had never had any clashes. When he complimented the ex-captain's intelligence and memory, he smiled shyly. 'I can actually understand why he might have been valuable to a bookie,' he said. 'His knowledge of conditions and their likely impact on a result was impeccable, his predictions often uncanny in their accuracy,' Ford added.

Fordie relayed an anecdote relating to the first test of the 2000 tour to India. The match was played in Mumbai and after giving the pitch one look, Cronjé predicted that it was going to be a low-scoring affair and that 225 would be a good score. India batted first and, believe it or not, they made exactly 225 – the highest innings total of the match.

Another aspect stressed by Fordie was Hansie Cronjé's extremely competitive nature. As far as he was concerned, there was never any reason to doubt this.

'What about Centurion?' I asked, referring to the incident in February 2000, where South Africa and England both forfeited an innings in a rain-plagued test match. As a consequence, the Proteas eventually ended up losing a match which had seemed dead and buried. Importantly, South Africa did not even need to take any chances as they had already wrapped up the series – but then again one can also argue that it didn't matter that much, as their series lead was unassailable.

But Cronjé's decision to declare was not criticised by Fordie. 'As captain, he had every right to do it. I'm sure he thought he could win the match. And remember, we very nearly did win it,' he said. No less than eight England wickets fell before they reached the target of 249 runs in 76 overs, and if Paul Adams had not broken a finger, Ford believed it might have been even closer.

But Graham Ford could not hide all his feelings. 'At the beginning of the season we mapped out our goals,' he said, 'and to top the rankings as the number one test-playing team was an important objective. By losing that match we gave up some valuable points in the process. After all, we did not *have* to make a game of it ... '

What also bothered Fordie, was the psychological impact of the victory. All of a sudden the English spirit was lifted in spite of losing the test series, and they could capitalise on this morale boost in the one-day series that followed. 'I will never forget how much it hurt to see the smiles on those English faces,' Ford said, 'or how "Sky Sports News" played it over and over and over.'

The last word on the Centurion test belongs to Bob Woolmer. In his book, he gives all credit to Cronjé for the declaration. But then again, it's easy for him to speak: he was no longer the coach; he had no remaining responsibility to manage the consequences.

* * * * *

One person not afraid to offer his opinion about the Hansie Cronjé affair is Professor Tim Noakes. A medical doctor by profession, he became a household name in South Africa in the 80s, as a specialist commentator of the Comrades Marathon. Noakes has completed this 90-kilometre ultra-marathon, run between Durban and Pietermaritzburg by more than 10,000 participants annually, no less than seven times himself – achieving a coveted silver medal on four of those occasions.

He is the co-founder, with Morné du Plessis, of the Sports Science Institute of South Africa, where he works as the Discovery Health Professor of Exercise and Sports Science at the University of Cape Town.

In 1985, Noakes published the first edition of his landmark work, entitled *Lore of Running*. The book soon achieved near-cult status in the running fraternity worldwide. Noakes is currently working on its fourth edition, which will be translated into German, Japanese and possibly Chinese. A celebration of running and science, the book also tells us much about Noakes, the person. In Chapter One, for example, the author states that he mixes rather poorly and then only with people who are essentially introverts, like himself. Taken at face value, this makes one realise how strong Noakes's feelings must be, regarding the Hansie Cronjé affair, to have been quoted in the way that he has.

Tim Noakes has acknowledged publicly that, when he was one of the very first South Africans to take an unpopular stand on the Hansie Cronjé issue (one that originally offended perhaps 99% of cricket-loving South Africans), he could have been more circumspect in the language that he used. I still remember some of the views attributed to Noakes at the time, and, from the moment that I decided to write this book, I knew that he was one person I simply had to talk to. Was he quoted correctly? And if he was, why on earth did he harbour such strong feelings?

My chat with Tim was one of the highlights when writing this book. To start with, I had no idea about how best to approach him. The one thing I figured, was that it would probably prove futile to try and arrange an interview through his secretary, as she would probably be quite well trained in shielding her celebrity boss from Nosey Parkers such as myself. Fortunately I live quite close to his office and I decided to follow the squatting approach: if I just went there and sat around long enough he would hopefully not be able to ignore me forever.

As it turned out, I could hardly have been more wrong. Tim's secretary was very helpful and when I explained my need for a short appointment, she suggested I discuss it with The Guru himself, sitting me down in his office until he returned from a lecture some twenty minutes later. What an office it was! How many people look out over Table Mountain on the one side and a brewery on the other? And he doesn't even drink.

The office was filled with books, more books and lots of memorabilia. Athletics, cricket, rugby and soccer all featured strongly. In one corner was displayed the front cover of a fake *Playboy* magazine: Noakes and some scantily clad ladies had been transposed onto the cover photograph. A humorous reference to his book appeared next to it. In another corner there was a full-size Salim Malik cricket bat in a huge frame, signed by all the members of the 1996 World Cup squad. The bat and a picture of Noakes with Paul Adams and Shane Warne, as well as a picture of his father's 1931 High School cricket team, are the only cricket momentoes that remain in the office. How ironic, I thought: not only that captain Hansie Cronjé's autograph should be right at the top of the Malik bat, but indeed that Malik himself is someone who's been banned for life from Pakistani cricket on the grounds of involvement in betting activities.

Professor Noakes finally walked into his office. No, he wasn't really in a position to talk about it. Yes, he had been quoted correctly. We started chatting …

Tim began telling me how his friendship with Bob Woolmer led to his initial involvement with the South African cricket team. 'To understand my position on this whole affair, you have first to know how and why I, a runner with little understanding of cricket, first became involved with the national cricket team. Shortly after Woolmer was appointed as coach to the Proteas, he approached me, and began to discuss his ideas of how we could together use science to improve the performance of international cricketers. Bob is genuinely one of the most innovative coaches in any sport that I have had the privilege to meet. So I was naturally flattered that he should consider asking my opinion, particularly as I had not the slightest clue about the subtleties of cricket.

'Then, in about August 1995, together with the team physiotherapist, Craig Smith, and the fitness consultant, Paddy Upton, Bob came to my office in Newlands, and asked whether I would consider coming to the 1996 World Cup as team doctor for the South African team. I wanted to know why this was necessary, to which Bob replied that he felt that if I were present, I could begin to learn the nuances of the game. This was going to be important for achieving the ultimate goal, which was to win the 1999 World Cup by out-thinking the opposition, especially the then World Cup holders, Sri Lanka, as well as the perennial enemy, Australia. Inasmuch as a scientific approach might provide the tiny advantage that differentiates the winners from the also-rans, so Bob's aim was to leave nothing to chance; no possible advantage unexplored.

'So, it was on that understanding – that here was a long-term plan to use science to help South African cricket reach a new level never before imagined in this country – that I finally, and somewhat reluctantly, agreed to Bob's request. And whilst I greatly enjoyed the 1996 World Cup, it was not an easy, uncomplicated experience that one would readily accept a second time.

'I have written on those experiences and expressed my high regard for the players of whom we expect to perform daily miracles on the cricket field, despite being away from home, in difficult circumstances, for very prolonged periods. I learnt on that tour that I would not have been able to do what our international cricketers do on a regular basis. And so my respect for those players grew proportionately, along with the desire to be of whatever assistance I could be, in helping them to achieve their ultimate reward in cricket – the 1999 Cricket World Cup.'

At this point, Noakes interrupted himself to relay an anecdote. He told me how he'd suggested writing a book about the players and their experiences at the 1996 World Cup. After initial agreement, he was told a couple of weeks into the tour that it was probably not such a good idea. During the tour, Hansie Cronjé approached Noakes and said to him in the context of a possible book: 'One day when I retire from cricket, I'll tell you a thing or two.' To this day, Noakes has wondered what exactly Cronjé might have been referring to.

'So it was during that time that Bob, with minor input from me, began to plot the way he was going to take international cricket to another dimension, not just in South Africa, but ultimately, as the rest of the world realised what had happened, also internationally. Besides his emphasis on fitness and innovative skill-training methods, we discussed plans to introduce some new technologies to South African cricket; technologies that were just then becoming adaptable to sport. These included game analysis, so that the patterns of play of the key opposing players could be logged between 1996 and 2000; the use of high-speed cameras to produce a three-dimensional view of the hand actions of key opposition bowlers, so that their difficult deliveries could be more easily identified by the South African batters; and the redesign of key equipment including pads, gloves and helmets, so that all functioned more effectively.

'In order to maximise our advantage, we even formed a Cricket Research Committee, that brought together all the best South African minds in the field. And we met on a regular basis. Like Bob, I believe that if you stay still in any area of human endeavour, the opposition soon slips by. And if you don't go with all your passion and commitment, then you will also not be successful.'

Noakes hardly paused to catch his breath before continuing. 'Because I believe that Bob has an unequalled ability to identify what is important in cricket, together with my confidence that he would get the job done, I committed myself passionately and emotionally to the Proteas and the ultimate goal of winning the 1999 World Cup. For I was certain that if Bob's ideas were embraced and supported then, for once, the Australians would be the ones doing the catching up. What's more, I was certain that the general South African morale would probably need an uplift by 1999, and that there would be nothing better than victory in the Cricket World Cup which, in my view, was entirely attainable. Unfortunately it never worked out that way. And the question that still needs to be answered to my satisfaction is: Why not?

'I have my views on what went wrong, and I described them in a coded way in the introduction to Bob Woolmer's book. His view is also ably expressed in that book, but because what he wrote was completely unbelievable to most when the book was published a few months before Hansiegate exploded, few may have understood or given any credence to what he was really trying to say. Also because his career is in cricket, he is not at liberty to express exactly what he might be thinking at all times. South African sport is so complex that a single wrong phrase can earn eternal damnation. So only those with nothing to lose are really free ever to express their true feelings.'

By now, I could tell that Tim had really warmed up; he was using facial expressions and gestures like the skilled orator that he is. He must be a heck of a lecturer, I thought to myself.

'During all this time, I had the opportunity to observe Hansie Cronjé in the detail that the general public have only recently enjoyed with the television broadcasts of the King Commission, and the interviews that Cronjé has since given on television and in the print media. I also applied my training to interpret his moods, his actions and his words. One forms an opinion of someone not on the basis of a single defining event, but as a result of many interactions; each of which is pretty inconsequential by itself. Your opinion is then based on the sum of those interactions.'

Tim Noakes told me how he agreed to contribute to Hansie Cronjé's benefit publication, which was published in 1997. It is quite telling, however, that in a publication of such obvious flattering nature, Noakes managed to write an article of 370 words without once referring to Cronjé. He writes about the triumphs and tribulations of a touring team (as discussed above), about the unrealistic expectations of the supporting public, even about the atmosphere in the national stadium in Karachi. But not once does he mention the South African captain, the very subject of the publication – a bit like the obituary written for the Unknown Soldier in which the fatal battle is discussed, yet the corpse remains unidentified.

Noakes continued. 'There was one seminal and defining event which occurred during the first test on the 1997 tour of Pakistan. Even though I was not present when it happened, the outcome did certainly involve me and proved the death knell for the scientific approach that Bob and I were trying to develop in order to take South African cricket forward.' Noakes would not elaborate on what this event was.

'So already in 1997, just 18 months after I had travelled with the team to the 1996 Cricket World Cup, it was clear to me that events had overtaken us. As a consequence, Bob's dream of using innovation to beat Sri Lanka and the Australians in order to win the 1999 World Cup, was increasingly unlikely to be realised. I knew then that Australia, who had been lagging far behind the innovations as introduced by Bob, would probably seize the opportunity and rapidly overtake us well before the tournament.'

Tim Noakes turned to the 1999 World Cup semi-final against Australia at Edgbaston. 'I was in the crowd, courtesy of a cricket conference at which I had been one of the speakers. I was as devastated as anyone by the loss, and could not sleep that night. My devastation was for Bob, as I believe that he is the best technical cricket coach in the world. He lifted South African cricket to a new level in the one-day game between 1995 and 1999, to the extent that his team was voted international cricket team of the year. I therefore believed that he deserved to reap the reward of having his team win the tournament. And for the players who had all played so brilliantly – with passion and commitment that was absolutely breathtaking. People like Kallis, Klusener, Pollock, Donald, Rhodes and Gibbs. Not to mention also, the rest of the team and the administrators throughout South Africa who had contributed to get us there in the first place.'

Noakes got a distant look in his eyes. 'It had been a supreme privilege to be present at what has since become known as one of the greatest games of cricket of all time. But the next day, after I had digested the loss, I came to terms with it on the grounds that if we had won, despite discarding the vision that Woolmer had introduced, and which I so passionately believed in, then perhaps that dated approach would have become the norm; probably to the long-term detriment of South African cricket.

'When the news broke that Cronjé had been involved with bookies for some time, even before the World Cup, and perhaps as far back as 1995, I was absolutely devastated. To have lost the World Cup because a dated and conservative approach had been adopted, purely out of ignorance, is one thing. It is not the first nor will it be the last time that this error has been made, either in sport or in business, with predictable consequences. But to lose for any other reason is just not acceptable. It will take time for the hurt of that lost opportunity to dissipate. And it will only really occur when we finally learn the complete truth.'

Noakes reflected on the ups and downs of his involvement with the Proteas. 'We dedicate our lives to these athletes,' he said, the frustration evident. 'I have 31 years of real experience in the sports sciences; they get it at no cost. And then the support that we have to offer ends up being dismissed and undermined on false grounds. First me, and then Bob.'

When Tim Noakes talked about Bob Woolmer, he became quite emotional. 'Bob is an innovator and a deep thinker,' Noakes repeated, emphatically. 'There may well have been some valid grounds to criticise him, but certainly not enough to force him out. Forcing Bob to seek employment in England was not in the long-term interests of South African cricket, in my view.'

Even though Tim Noakes revealed a lot in his conversations, there were some details that he was unwilling to discuss or reveal. 'What I learnt from this event is that "truth" in public life is not the same as the truth we attempt to uncover daily in the science that we practise. There are too many factors that impinge on what eventually is revealed.

'There remain some questions that I would like to see answered, and perhaps a measure of truth will still emerge from this tragedy. In my opinion, the jury is still out on exactly what Cronjé really did. Until the evidence that the Indian police have collected is exposed to the legal process, there can be no final judgement on the extent of his innocence.'

Discussing his assessment of Hansie Cronjé's personality, Tim Noakes speculated that the prospect of anonymity could be more of a 'problem' to Cronjé than all of the trouble that he might be in. That is why he bounced back so quickly with television interviews and the announcement of his own book, for example. 'If anything like this ever happened to me, you'd never see me again – I'd be in Papua New Guinea within 24 hours!' Noakes said with a characteristically boyish grin.

He looked at his watch; he had another appointment in five minutes. 'Finally, I would really like to know why the South African cricket writers, the supposed authorities, never once questioned, in a critical way, what went wrong in those final two games against Australia in the 1999 World

Cup. Also, how this should have been interpreted as a true measure of the captain's leadership skills, as well as his ability to cope with the stresses of the World Cup.

'Much was made of Gibbs's dropped catch at Headingly, but, in my view, both games against Australia could, and should, still have been won, even accounting for that error. We live with a strange sporting press in this country – the rugby press is often too destructive for the good of the sport; in contrast, in this matter, the cricket writers come out as being too meek and submissive, in my view. For example, one of our senior cricket journalists told me that after he had seen what I had said, the scales fell from his eyes and he gained a new perspective, hidden from his understanding for more than five years!'

Noakes and I both stood up; he had to attend to his next meeting. On the way out, he shared a final thought: 'Nobody ever reported the mood change that I perceived Cronjé to have undergone in the six months leading up to the 1999 World Cup; a change since acknowledged by the person who should know best – his mother.' Noakes referred to the M-Net interview with Mike Haysman, where San-Marie Cronjé spoke about her son's body language, saying that she could sense something had been wrong. In the same interview Hansie's father, Ewie, mentioned that his son was at a low every time he took money.

'There is a saying that moods are the way in which we speak of our distress – you can find it in my book,' Tim Noakes added, almost whimsically. Afterwards, I would confirm the quote in *Lore of Running*. It is attributed to Lord Moran, who was a regimental doctor in the First World War, later to become Winston Churchill's personal physician. Moran elaborated by saying that it is too late to save a pilot by the time a change is evident in his behaviour on the ground.

Noakes concluded. 'One never knows … maybe if we had read his moods more carefully and understood their meaning, we might have prevented this tragedy from ever happening. And with a proper intervention we would have spared Cronjé and his team the lifelong consequences of whatever might have taken place.'

We shook hands and say good-bye. The appointment I never had, had gone on for an hour and a half.

'Perhaps the basis for that defeat will eventually be acknowledged,' Tim Noakes writes about the World Cup semi-final, in the introduction to

Bob Woolmer's book. Having heard from the man himself about his views relating to the national team's build-up between 1997 and 1999, I now had a much better idea of what Noakes might really have meant when he wrote those words.

In closing the discussion of Tim Noakes and his views, I cannot help but return to *Lore of Running* again. Running, Noakes says, has taught him about real honesty. 'There is, you see, no luck in running. Results cannot be faked and there is no-one but yourself to blame when things go wrong.'

Little wonder, I realise, that Noakes would have such strong feelings – especially if he believes that an athlete might have entertained thoughts about betraying the trust of a nation, enriching himself in the process.

*　*　*　*　*

Ray McCauley has been called the Raymond Ackerman of evangelism, the Sol Kerzner of religion and the Superman of spirituality. He refers to himself as the unofficial chaplain to the South African cricket, rugby and soccer teams. And he has been a close friend and personal adviser to Hansie Cronjé for the last eight years.

Pastor Ray McCauley is the founder, anchor and public face of Rhema Ministries, the fastest-growing religious group in South Africa. From zero to 25,000 active members in only twenty years – during a period in which many other churches have seen dwindling numbers – is certainly no mean feat. Today it is a big business, employing a full-time staff of 750 which includes more than 500 social workers. The Rhema premises in Randburg reminds one of an office park, complete with security guards at the gate, more security at reception, and building after building spread across an expanse of some thirteen hectares – providing space not only for traditional church activities, but also for recording studios, sports facilities, shops and a café.

It was Ray McCauley who was woken up by Hansie Cronjé in the early hours of the morning on 11 April 2000, when the now ex-cricket captain faxed through his first confession. It was Ray McCauley who cancelled all meetings and flew to Cape Town that same day, in order to be with Cronjé at the first press conference. And it has been the same Ray McCauley standing by the cricketer through everything that has happened in the meantime, despite the fact that the pastor himself also had to deal with the fact that he had been lied to by Cronjé on at least two separate occasions in the process. Clearly, Ray McCauley was an important person to interview, in order to try and understand another piece of the Hansie puzzle.

It wasn't easy to obtain time in Pastor Ray's diary. During my first phone call, I was referred from one secretary to another, all speaking in similarly mellifluous voices, only to be told that I needed to explain the nature of my request in writing. 'Oh yes, and Pastor Ray will be overseas for the next ten days; when he comes back, he's only here for two days before he has to go to Portugal again.' I wasn't too hopeful, but I sent a letter in any case. Lo and behold, a few weeks, phone calls and e-mails later I received my reply: 'Pastor Ray can see you next Thursday at 14:30.' Cancel all other appointments, book flights to Johannesburg; when The Pastor summons, you have to go!

I was escorted to Ray McCauley's spacious office by his Publicity Affairs Officer, Reverend Ron Steele (an experienced journalist), who sat with us for the duration of our chat.

'How would you like to be described, Pastor Ray?' I began, whilst appreciating the tasteful interior design, the certificates on the wall and the sweeping views across Randburg's industrial area.

'Well, it'll probably surprise people when I say that I'm spiritual, rather than religious. In my heart I'm still a body-builder who can be mates with the guys. I'm an extrovert, I'm happy-go-lucky and I'm always positive – except after last year's cricket World Cup ...'

Pastor Ray proceeded to tell me that the World Cup defeat was the one thing Hansie Cronjé also never recovered from. 'And when he got low, he got really low – like most people who have such strong personalities. Of course, I've seen him moody, often. I have, after all, been his chaplain for many years.'

I asked McCauley how it came about that he became the team chaplain.

'Well, it was Kepler Wessels who originally invited me on tour, to do Bible study with some of the guys. But when Hansie became captain he took it one step further and invited me to also take responsibility for motivational sessions with the whole team. Are you with me?'

In every one of his answers, Ray McCauley slowly builds up to a

113

crescendo. As he nears the end of each response, he starts talking not only a little faster, but also a little louder. Then he leans forward, clenches his fists, opens his eyes wide and looks straight into your soul, ending with 'Are you with me?' or 'Do you hear what I'm saying?'.

It was quite intimidating. What do you expect from a voice that can fill a stadium, with body language to match (especially considering that this particular body once won third prize in the Mr Universe competition)? I think I now understand why he has been so successful at converting sceptics to religion, and motivating sports stars to take on the opposition. It's probably easier to turn your back on a world of sin, or to face up to Waqar Younis in full flight, than to stand up to McCauley and say, 'No, Pastor Ray, as a matter of fact, I don't follow.'

McCauley has been travelling around the world with South Africa's cricketers and other sports stars for a decade now. But his status as chaplain to the teams is essentially a self-appointed one, reinforced by friendships with people like Hansie Cronjé. 'I do it because it's a calling; no sports body has ever paid for a plane ticket or hotel room of mine,' he insisted.

Asking the pastor about his views on the Hansie saga, he gave me a structured, three-pronged response, like a carefully prepared sermon. 'Firstly, I never expected it, not in a million years. So when the news first broke, I felt let down; I was disappointed, I was shocked. And it was an even bigger shock when his first confession ended up not being truthful either. It really hurt.

'Secondly, I think he could have been more wise in his dealings in the interim. I don't think, for example, that he should have taken money for the M-Net interviews. I know how much he got, but I won't disclose it. I don't think he should have done anything like appointing promotional managers or image consultants or whatever, until after the King Commission was over. I told him that repentance should go hand in hand with a change from how you used to be, to how you should be.

'But thirdly, I want to stress that I stand by him and that I think he is a first-class individual. He went on crusades with me on many occasions; he always helped the kids, and he was extremely well-mannered. In fact, he showed so much respect to others that I often criticised him on his correctness, more than anything else. He never swore or got drunk. He always kept his promises. He's the kind of guy that would always be early

114

for appointments. And, except for this, he's never lied to me ... are you with me?'

We discussed other aspects of the Cronjé personality. 'He hates criticism; he's an absolute perfectionist. He is very structured and likes to control things. We used to sit down and map out five-year goals for him. And he would stick to them – weekly. This included not only planned achievements, but it went down to the level of training programmes, target weights, pulse rates and the like.'

Pastor Ray continued. 'He was like a son in my house. I remember one evening when he rocked up at my place at seven o'clock in the evening, saying how low he was after his knee operation. He was nearly in tears. We prayed and spent time together ... eventually at midnight he jumped into the pool and started exercising. After that, he got out and ran around the garden – he was fine.'

With a mixture of pride and sadness, Ray McCauley pointed out to me how Hansie had told him he wouldn't have made the mistakes that he did, if only the pastor had been with the team in India. 'He needs me now, more than ever, you know. That's why I'll continue to fulfil my pastoral function until the whole matter is resolved. Doesn't matter what people say. Do you know what I mean?'

I asked Ray McCauley whether he thought Hansie Cronjé had been totally honest in the end. 'Yes,' he responded, 'he certainly answered all questions truthfully. But I'm not sure that he's been asked everything.'

So why didn't he volunteer the information, if there was anything else that he might have known? 'You can blame the lawyers for that,' the pastor said. 'Obviously Hansie has to listen to them when he appears before a judge.'

Interestingly, McCauley was also the person who was first approached by Clive Rice about a possible book deal for Hansie to tell his side of the story. The approach was eventually passed on to Cronjé himself but, in spite of talking to Hansie on a regular basis, the pastor didn't know what the current status of the book was. 'But in the end, it'll probably all come down to who's prepared to pay the most,' he conceded.

What did the future hold for Hansie Cronjé? Not a career in Rhema, according to McCauley; Hansie was destined for the business world. 'But I guess a lot may depend on what might come out at the King Commission.'

Chatting briefly about his own background, Pastor Ray confirmed that he had had a turbulent childhood, and that his father was a professional bookmaker. But that had nothing to do with the fact that he and Hansie Cronjé would relate so well to one another in years to come ...

Ray McCauley had many amusing and interesting anecdotes to tell about his time with the South African cricket team. With a huge grin on his face, arms waving like an octopus falling out of a tree, he told me about all the work he did in counselling Daryll Cullinan before the batsman would face up to Shane Warne. 'Eventually I gave up and said, "Just close your eyes, Daryll, and hit!"' He also told me about his unique friendship with Pat Symcox, who would sometimes join the Bible study sessions on tour with a cigarette in one hand and a beer in the other, saying to the rest of them, 'Now let me tell you okes how these things really work.' And then he would proceed to do so, some strong language mixed in for good measure.

On my way out, I asked Pastor Ray if the 'What Would Jesus Do' wrist band, as worn by Hansie, was a Rhema-endorsed product? 'No,' he said, with a smile so wide it wouldn't fit onto the faces of too many other people, 'it's an international thing – but I'll tell you what I think the answer is in this case: Jesus certainly wouldn't have spoken to those guys from India!' After that, I got whisked away as efficiently as I had been brought into the office in the first place.

* * * * *

Imtiaz Patel used to be the Director of Professional Cricket at the United Cricket Board of South Africa. In plain English, this means that Imtiaz basically acted as Dr Ali Bacher's right-hand man until he was lured away by SuperSport, the pay television station M-Net's exclusive sports channel, where he serves as Director of Enterprises today.

Although Imtiaz got to know Hansie Cronjé quite well over the years, the relationship wasn't as close as it might have been, because the interaction with the national team itself was one of the responsibilities that Ali Bacher never delegated. Yet despite the relatively limited contact between the two of them, Patel believes that there was always a lot of trust between himself and Cronjé.

They also did a number of things together on the cricket development front: Imtiaz remembered how, on one particular occasion, Cronjé had driven all the way from Bloemfontein – by himself – just in order to assist at a training clinic in Sharpeville. And there were no television cameras that day …

Patel also told me a story going back to when the sponsor of Free State cricket renewed its deal with the province in 1998. At the function, attended by players, officials and businessmen, Hansie immediately jumped in behind the bar and started serving drinks. 'It always stayed with me, you know, and it just showed me the way that he had been brought up,' he says.

But the one thing Imtiaz noted, was how important control was to Cronjé. Even so, Hansie would always signal it in an understated way. 'He would often just make a fleeting remark, like "Don't you think Ali has too much power?", changing the topic shortly afterwards.'

Patel spoke further about a few occasions at which Hansie Cronjé approached him regarding prospective business deals – all of them internet-based. The first one went back to the second half of 1999; another took place during the Emirates all-rounder championship at Newlands, at the beginning of April 2000 (two days before the first news about the Indian phone transcripts broke). Imtiaz elaborated. 'That last time, he told me he already had technology partners lined up in India.'

Imtiaz and I proceeded to chat in general terms about match-fixing in world cricket. 'Look, some of the things coming out now aren't really surprising. There is a journalist in London who's been telling us for years about stuff that was going on in other countries. Naively, we just never believed that it would affect us in this country, in the way that it did. But I certainly don't think the whole sport is corrupt. I just think there's probably a lot that's been going on – all controlled by quite a small group of people at the centre.'

And then Imtiaz ended off with a typically pragmatic analogy. 'It's like apartheid, you know, it was such a powerful thing. But if you analyse it, it was really driven by just a handful of politicians who felt strongly enough about the concept, and for a long time they had enough power that they could institutionalise it. Most of the people didn't even agree with it in their hearts – and I'm not talking about the disenfranchised majority here, I'm talking about their own constituency – that's why the transition to the New South Africa ended up being so much more seamless than what many people had feared. So, yes, this match-fixing issue is like apartheid: it's a big thing and it's a terrible thing, but I honestly think in the end it's only a small number of individuals.'

*   *   *   *   *

What are the main conclusions that one can draw about Hansie Cronjé from speaking to a coach, a medical consultant, a spiritual adviser and an administrator, a few ex-players and a physiotherapist?

To be fair, most of them had many good things to say about the man. He was a good captain with a phenomenal cricket brain, who certainly built up good relationships with a lot of people in the world of cricket.

A theme that was prevalent in nearly every discussion, however, was the extent to which control was vitally important to Cronjé. One can argue that he became so powerful in the end, that he started believing he could basically do whatever he wanted to. It's easy to understand that the difference between what's wrong and what's right could perhaps get blurred in the process.

Related to this is the fact that Hansie Cronjé did not take kindly to criticism. This is probably typical of someone who is excessively power-hungry: if you believe that you're the one who should always control matters, what right does anyone else have to question the way in which you do things?

It also seems as if there was quite a lot of evidence concerning the ex-captain's love of money. His business mind had evidently been working overtime over a protracted period. This raises questions about the extent to which he was always a hundred percent focused on the job at hand – to perform for his country as a batsman, a bowler and a captain – to the highest possible standard.

Furthermore, the man certainly had his moods. We all 'throw our toys' sometimes, but from what some people say – even those close to him – the placid image that he portrayed to the outside world was often quite different to the real Cronjé.

In summary, it appears that there were a number of important signals that were either missed, ignored or misinterpreted by the relevant cricket authorities. With the benefit of hindsight, a disaster might have been prevented if these signals had been properly read and acted upon. One can only hope that similar mistakes will not be made again.

5

The 1999 World Cup

The Darwin Awards are tongue-in-cheek accolades, presented periodically in the memory of those who improve the overall quality of the human race by removing themselves from it – consistent with the Charles Darwin theory of evolution. In short, the awards go to those who manage to cause their own demise in a way that is more amusing than it is intelligent. Like the motorcar driver who had a Tamagochi key ring: he was driving on the highway when the toy beeped for food, the driver fidgeted to 'feed' it lest it lose a life, and crashed the car in the process – the Tamagochi survived, the driver didn't.

I couldn't help thinking of the Darwin Awards when watching the final round of the British Open golf tournament at Carnoustie on Sunday the 24th of July 1999. Jean van de Velde, the charismatic Frenchman and natty dresser who was never supposed to be in contention, contrived to squander a three-shot lead with only one hole to play. Many commentators agree that this dreaded day might well be the last opportunity van de Velde will ever have of winning one of golf's major tournaments.

I shook my head in disbelief. However, I soon reminded myself that an incident like that was the very essence of sport. We love sport not simply because it *can* happen; we love sport because it often does happen when we least expect it to.

Our addiction to the sports we love can often be explained on emotional and psychological grounds, rather than the physical. It is quite simply a function of the fix we get when we – or those we support –

119

conquer the odds and achieve an unlikely victory: a victory either over the tremendous inherent challenge contained in an event itself, or over a competing field which may be considered to be superior by many.

It is for this very reason that we instinctively back the underdog whenever our own team is not playing; we continue believing that we might be rewarded by witnessing one of those special moments in sport when the improbable does in fact happen. After all, if we didn't believe that sheer talent and preparation could sometimes lose out to the bounce of the ball, there would simply be no reason to continue watching the inevitable unfold when a favourite's in the lead.

Unfortunately, the French golfer's imaginative act of self-destruction in and around the Barry Burn on that fateful Sunday afternoon also happened to remind me of an equally devastating incident some five and a half weeks earlier: the day South Africa snatched defeat from the jaws of victory in the semi-final of the Cricket World Cup against Australia at Edgbaston.

Just like van de Velde, the way it ended at Edgbaston 'was never supposed to happen'. Like van de Velde, for many in the South African cricket team there will probably not be another chance. And just like in the case of van de Velde, what had transpired could afterwards only be rationalised on philosophical grounds.

I vividly remember the golfer's magnanimous comments twenty-four hours later. 'Nobody died ... it's only a game ... it's only a name on a trophy ...' Show me a good loser and I'll show you someone who always loses, they say.

After the World Cup semi-final, Steve Waugh, for once, sympathised with a team he helped defeat in a match which he said was the greatest he ever played in. ' ... the sun will come up tomorrow; life goes on ...'

Tell that to someone like Jonty Rhodes, a player who'd already been at the receiving end of bad fortune in two previous World Cup tournaments. Nobody in cricket would ever doubt Jonty's big match temperament. Twice before, however, the best fielder in the world – boisterous as a cocker spaniel before a long-awaited walk – had to reconcile himself with failure when success appeared to be so tangibly close.

In 1992, when South Africa lost to England in the semi-final, they could console themselves by blaming it on the rain. In 1996, when South Africa lost against the West Indies in the quarter-final, they could simply count themselves unlucky because they happened to strike Brian Lara on one of his memorable 'on' days. But by the time that the Proteas arrived at the 1999 World Cup in England, all excuses had run out and the day of reckoning arrived.

The South Africans were quite simply the best team in the world at the time. In the eighteen months prior to the tournament, the team had secured a flurry of victories. They beat Sri Lanka in a test series at home. They trumped England in a one-day series in England. They destroyed the West Indies on South African soil in five tests as well as a one-day series. They pipped New Zealand on their own turf in both one-day internationals and test matches. And they won the Wills International Cup, a mini World Cup knock-out tournament held in Bangladesh, involving all the major cricket nations.

The only blemish during the entire period was a test series lost to England amidst some controversy: 'everybody' agreed that the umpires were squarely to blame for the defeat. Remember the match at Headingley involving Javed Akhtar of Pakistan where South Africa saw eight of its players dismissed leg before wicket in the space of four days?

Yet there remained some unfinished business: they still needed to win the 1999 World Cup to finally prove the point of their ultimate supremacy. They needed to prove it to their detractors who'd long been haunting them with accusations that the team wasn't mentally strong enough to handle the really big occasions. They needed to prove it to their supporters who – for political reasons – had to live through sixteen years' frustration of not even having a team at the first four World Cup tournaments, only to realise over the course of the next two competitions that the devastation of losing is nearly as bad. But most of all they needed to prove it to themselves, for they were the ones that had been *living* the dream, and they were the ones that would forever have to continue living with themselves – whatever the final outcome.

So why did they fail?

At the commencement of the 1999 World Cup tournament in England, with the South Africans quite understandably instilled as odds-on favourites, there was just no way that my mother, the fanatic, was going to miss any moment of it. I arranged for the two of us to go on a ten-day SuperSport Travel tour, taking in the opening match between hosts England and World Cup holders Sri Lanka at Lord's, as well as South

Africa's first three matches. Quite a strange couple we were, the 72-year-old woman and her 34-year-old last born.

I soon learnt that most people who go on these 'supporters' tours' have some or other idiosyncrasy. Whereas normal people go to work, come home and watch the game on television, the groupies who follow their team around all seem to lead lives that are somewhat more interesting. The mainstay of our party of fourteen was a semi-retired and extremely entertaining insurance salesman from Johannesburg's Southern Suburbs, who carried with him a pre-made canvas banner depicting a storming rhinoceros and the words, 'Make Way for SA'. The group also included a sophisticated couple who owned a chicken farm in Northern Kwa-Zulu Natal, a professional golfer and her mother, an elderly couple who had lost a son in a car crash, a young man who had decided to take a few years off to wander around the world following the untimely death of his young wife, and a middle-aged bachelor with a loud voice and a great thirst, whose eventual departure from the British Isles must be rued by brewers and publicans to this day.

It's funny what you get to know about a bunch of complete strangers when travelling with them for a few days. And it's very interesting to notice not only how quickly people begin forming opinions of one another, but also how soon they begin discussing these with others assumed to be of like mind. This was a ten-day crash course in human nature against the backdrop of warm beer, roast beef and Yorkshire pudding, with a bit of cricket thrown in for good measure!

Not much to report about the opening match at Lord's on the 14th of May 1999. An extremely forgettable opening ceremony with a few balloons and some low-key fireworks. A most important toss in overcast conditions after three days of rain – whoever bowled first could hardly lose the match. In the event Alec Stewart won the toss and got the Man of the Match award for that (although his three catches and 88 runs might also have played a small part in the accolade). Sri Lanka's batting never quite got going and England's performance was clinical.

I must confess that my mother and I didn't last the whole distance that day. She was quite tired following the twelve-hour overnight flight from Africa, and I was bored stiff. I wasn't alone either: I'm sure I spotted Graeme Hick yawning in between hitting sixes. We left with about 10 overs to go and eventually witnessed England's inevitable victory on television in a pub near Marble Arch.

The next day we got up early to drive down to Brighton. South Africa was playing India at Hove, a quaint little field on the outskirts of this rather sleepy seaside resort. When you visit the homepage of the English Cricket Board on the internet, you are referred from the Grounds section to a website entitled Local Information on Hove Cricket Ground. Click on it and you will find the description, 'Hove is famous for its deckchairs where spectators can sit in the sun and watch a day's cricket. The current capacity at Hove is only 5500.'

That's it.

Having been there, I understand. In fact I admire the author for successfully stretching the description to more than twenty words, given that his brief was probably not to be overly critical. It is small, old and more than slightly dilapidated; the kind of field and pavilion you'd expect to find at a high school in a small town in South Africa. And not a very good high school at that, I might add. But I imagine that this is what the Old Country is all about: it reeks of history, and you can't always have your cake and eat it.

I am told that the first county game was played at Hove as far back as 1872, which is more than a decade before the documented history of an important city like Johannesburg began, for those who may have wondered. The scoreboard was constructed in 1934. What is more the pity, is that it appears not to have been upgraded or maintained ever since.

An additional issue that needs pointing out, is that the slope of the ground is more severe than anything I've ever witnessed in cricket. It basically runs straight down to the sea. If ever it snowed in Brighton, I wouldn't be at all surprised if the locals constructed a T-bar and began selling Hove ski passes to winter tourists.

Due to the intimate nature of such a small ground, there couldn't be anything but a carnival atmosphere during the match between South Africa and India. Our group was stuck in a corner, directly behind a group of vocal Indian supporters. A few of us responded by being vocal right back. The fact that there were no skirmishes on the day was a credit to our collective good nature and sportsmanship. One year later, when cricket administrators and government officials of the two countries were completely at odds during the Cronjé affair, this spirit of friendship

123

seemed all the more remarkable.

The players on the field contributed in no small measure to the special atmosphere. India set a respectable target of 254, and South Africa made rather heavy weather, until Jonty Rhodes chipped in with a whirlwind 39 not out off only 31 balls. Lance Klusener gave early notice of the formidable role he would play over the course of the tournament, blasting three boundaries in the four balls that he faced (without being dismissed, of course).

All according to plan. My mother was happy: her team had won comfortably, and her favourite 'son' had made a reasonable contribution. Hansie Cronjé's 27 would eventually prove to be his second highest score of the tournament. Little did Mum know at this stage that she wouldn't see Cronjé hit another boundary in the remaining two matches that she was to witness.

But the match at Hove will best be remembered for a rather unique incident involving the same Mr Cronjé. The South African research team had for some time been working on new technology involving earpieces that enable the coach or captain to communicate with the players on the field as the game progresses; a concept long used in American football.

Not finding anything explicit in the laws of cricket that outlaw the concept – and following the old adage that it's easier to ask forgiveness than permission – the Proteas thought it appropriate to test their new toys in the match against India. Hansie Cronjé could be seen moving around with a strapped ear, looking like a secret service agent in a spy movie – sunglasses to boot! The authorities quickly found grounds to ban the technology for the rest of the tournament and the South African tactics were widely criticised as being opportunistic, naïve and even underhanded. But the technology is there, it works and it's still not clear why it can't be used; more than a year later, the matter remains essentially unresolved.

Off to Northampton for South Africa's next match, this time against Sri Lanka, on Wednesday the 19th of May 1999. After reading Hove's gem of a description, I couldn't help but pay another quick visit to the English Cricket Board's Grounds site on the internet. Clicking onto the Northampton County Ground, I was once again rewarded. 'Surrounded by red-brick terraced houses, this is a ground of character rather than beauty,' read the opening line. Shame. Most people I know would never forgive you if you ever said something like that about them. But once again, having been to the ground, I cannot argue with this comment.

This seemed like it was never going to be South Africa's day. Sri Lanka won the toss and put South Africa in to bat in overcast conditions; for the first couple of hours it was actually freezing. Two very dubious decisions by the television umpire followed. It started when Shaun Pollock was given out after quite clearly driving the ball into the ground, onto Ranatunga's leg at silly point and into the hands of Muralitharan. Two overs later, Daryll Cullinan received his marching orders when Vaas caught the ball at long off and flung it infield while falling over the boundary rope. The laws of cricket state that the fielder must have 'complete control of the further disposal of the ball ... within the field of play'. It's a moot point whether that means the player can legally offload the ball in desperation, a nano-second before completely losing his balance in an area normally reserved for spectators and hot-dog vendors.

By the way, if you ever thought that Mr Vaas had quite a short name for a Sri Lankan, think again. His full name happens to be Warnakulasuriya Patabendige Ushantha Joseph Chaminda Vaas. Dinkum, as they say in Australia. More initials than letters in the surname certainly takes some doing.

At 122 for 8, and with all 'recognised' batsmen back in the pavilion, the Proteas didn't look like they would get past the 150 mark. Mum was livid.

Enter Lance Klusener. Fortunately nobody told him that he didn't really count as a recognised batsman. After pottering about for a pedestrian 30 runs off the first 40 balls that he faced, he suddenly realised that the last over was under way and he was still 20 runs away from a half-century. No problem. Even as a South African, one couldn't help but feel some sympathy for Sri Lankan fast bowler WPUJC Vaas, watching his last 5 deliveries go for 4, 2, 4, 6 and 6. A lesser bowler might have gone for more.

When Sri Lanka came in to bat and lost their 4th wicket with the score at only 14, the match was all but over. Lance Klusener waited until the 26th over before his captain eventually called on him as the fifth bowler. He promptly cleaned up the tail, taking 3 wickets in 5.2 overs. No prizes for guessing who got the Man of the Match award.

Once again, all according to plan. After looking down-and-out earlier in the day, the South Africans beat Sri Lanka by a comfortable 89 runs.

Admittedly, my mother didn't have much to celebrate on the Cronjé front that day (he scored only 8 runs, and he didn't bowl). But we could always toast his captaincy whilst squeezing into a crowded pub, watching Zimbabwe pull off a surprise victory over India a little bit later.

Before we reached the pub, however, we officially began our quest for an all-important photograph of my mother and Hansie. When walking past the players' dressing rooms, we joined a large group of people waiting for the teams to appear. No such luck. After an hour we gave up; the only player to hang about outside and chat to people, was a short chap with curly, dark hair and a permanent grin. Most people didn't even recognise Nicky Bojé; his moment of fame was still a year away.

So back to London we went, for the vital clash between Cup favourites South Africa and the Old Enemy, hopeful hosts England. This would be the last match our group was to watch, and quite fittingly it took place at The Oval, the ground where a test series in England usually ends.

Steeped in history, the first ever test on English soil was played at The Oval in 1880; a match in which W.G. Grace scored a century on debut. England achieved both their highest ever test total (903/7 against Australia in 1938) as well as their lowest ever total on home soil (52 all out, again versus Australia, in 1948) at the ground. In an ironic twist, the top score in both these innings came from the bat of the same person, Len Hutton: 364 in 1938, and 30, ten years later. And finally, the low-scoring affair in 1948 also happened to be the last ever test match in which Donald Bradman played. History will show that, if only Bradman had scored 4 runs rather than the second ball duck that he did in fact achieve, his career average would have been 100.00 and not 99.94. Funny game, cricket.

From the moment our group of South Africans entered the ground on the 22nd of May 1999, all of us just knew: *this was going to be our day*. Some days at sports events are just like that: anyone who attended the opening match of the 1995 Rugby World Cup between South Africa and Australia at Newlands, for example, will know what I mean. *Today we could not lose*. The spectator can sense it in the way that sights and sounds combine on such a day; a mixture of urgency and excitement which is impossible to describe but easy to identify.

There seemed to be more South African flags than there were English supporters (later in the day, when English wickets started tumbling, I'm sure that actually turned out to be true). The entire side of The Oval beneath the gas tower was packed with Protea supporters.

An hour and a half before the match, the teams came onto the field to warm up. A lasting memory will always be Jonty Rhodes asking for some high ball catching practice. Corrie van Zyl hit one a bit too far, or so thought the few hundred spectators who were already beginning to fill the stands. Jonty turned around, ran like crazy and dived as if his life depended on it, holding onto the ball with outstretched fingers. Spontaneous, stupefied applause ... for catching practice! *Today we could not lose.* Later that day, Rhodes would be rewarded for his commitment when he managed to hang onto another memorable catch, first leaping high and palming the ball up with an outstretched left hand, and then, with both the fielder and ball plummeting to the ground, catching it on the second attempt.

Not even winning the toss and putting South Africa in to bat was going to help England. A Nelsonian opening partnership of 111 between Kirsten and Gibbs laid a solid enough foundation. Even when 5 wickets fell with only 35 more runs being added, all of us remained unmoved. In fact, we were just beginning to warm up. 'Zuluuuuu ...,' ten thousand rowdy South Africans chanted as Lance Klusener walked to the wicket. And 'Zuluuuuu ...,' we repeated, every time he calmly clobbered the ball to the boundary with so much force that I still wonder how the leather managed to stay on the ball. Another 48 runs in 40 balls, another occasion on which the white Zulu never looked like he would be dismissed, another Man of the Match award – it was on the verge of getting boring.

Once again, Hansie Cronjé's performance was unremarkable. He scored 16 runs, not reaching the boundary once. And he failed to introduce himself into the bowling attack later in the day.

When it was England's turn to bat, they quickly capitulated – their total of 103 the lowest ever in a one-day international against South Africa. The losing margin was a mammoth 122.

Afterwards, my mother and I (together with thousands of other South African supporters) stormed onto the playing surface for the awards ceremony. We were cheering and singing, and just hanging about – on a day like that you don't go home straight away. We were eventually joined by some of our heroes who came down from the dressing rooms to mix with the riffraff on the field. Mum got a beautiful photograph with a popular yet patient Jonty Rhodes; Herschelle Gibbs also came down, as did Nicky Bojé.

But where on earth was Hansie? I asked Nicky Bojé, always the approachable one, always the same. Having chatted to him at some length after the game in Northampton, I was starting to build up a bit of a personal relationship with him. 'Hansie will probably not come down,' he said, 'he doesn't really like this sort of thing.' The fact that there were thousands of fans who'd all travelled halfway around the world and spent a fortune just to be there, didn't seem to matter.

I explained to Nicky my need for a photograph of Hansie with my mother. Curiously, he actually seemed to understand. He told me the name of the hotel where the team was staying and suggested that I try the next morning at breakfast time. Armed with this piece of classified information, my mother and I left The Oval. She wasn't nearby when I chatted to Nicky; I didn't want to raise any undue expectations.

The following morning, we went to the Royal Garden Hotel in Kensington. Upon our arrival, who were standing outside but Shaun Pollock and Gary Kirsten, waiting for a lift to take them on a golf outing.

After taking the compulsory photographs of Mum with both of the players, I enquired as to the whereabouts of the South African captain. Inside, having breakfast, was the verdict. Thank goodness, I sighed. I was rather worried that we might actually miss him.

I left Mum in the lobby and went to the breakfast room to check that the Big Fish hadn't actually disappeared. And there he was, quietly sitting by himself, reading the newspaper. Bingo. Some of the other players were sitting around in groups of two and three, but the captain was probably not in the mood for company. Strange, I thought, surely a leader must spend time with his troops?

Much later, when researching this book, a number of people would confirm that Hansie would often spend time by himself on occasions such as this. If one wants to read anything into this behaviour, I believe that it adds some credence to a line of testimony which leads to the understanding that less people, rather than more, used to be involved in Cronjé's dealings with bookmakers.

It required some restraint, but I managed to withhold myself from pestering Hansie at the breakfast table. Instead I waited outside: except for an escape route though an obscure-looking fire exit, there was no way that he could avoid passing me on his way to the outside world.

After what felt like a couple of hours but probably wasn't more than about thirty minutes, Hansie Cronjé eventually made his appearance. I accosted him, introduced myself and declared my interest in a photographic moment, all in one breath – I've never been a slouch when it comes to talking. OK, he said, not looking overly ecstatic about the idea, but first he needed to get some stuff from his room. 'Just wait here,' he said, before getting into the elevator.

I fetched my mother and we continued the vigil. Another thirty-five minutes went by. This time I actually measured it. Every time the lift arrived on the ground floor, Mum would excitedly say the same thing. 'This must be him now!' Eventually, she had to be right of course. 'See, I told you so!'

Thinking back to that wait, I vividly remember how anticipation on my part slowly turned to irritation. Did Hansie Cronjé not actually want us to take the photograph? Why did we have to wait so long? This sense of frustration was brought particularly into focus a year later, when Cronjé testified before the King Commission about occasions when he willingly would go to the rooms of strangers, thinking they might be after an autograph or a picture. Taking this evidence at face value, I wish I could say that our experience reflected a similar level of accessibility on the part of the ex-captain.

When Hansie eventually stepped out of that lift, golf bag over one shoulder and change of clothing over the other, I realised that the moment of truth had finally arrived. It was like my life flashed before me; so many things went through my mind. What if there's no film in the camera? What if the flash doesn't work? What if…?

I took a few deep breaths, steadied myself and took the first picture. Hansie Cronjé immediately turned away and tried to excuse himself, but my mother would have nothing of it – his smile in that first picture failed to comply with her considerable expectations. 'Come on, Hansie, I came a long way just for this picture,' she said, grabbing him by the arm, forcing an even wider grin from him for the second photograph.

At last we had it. Like a golfer achieving a hole-in-one or a fisherman catching a marlin, there was nothing left for Mum. The two of us could go back home in peace, reflecting on a mission accomplished.

Following the rest of the tournament on television obviously made for a very different experience compared to actually being at the grounds during those first few matches. What one loses in atmosphere is compensated for somewhat by the benefit of replays and slow-motion analysis. Whereas stadium spectators are typically quite emotional and passionate, those who view the game on the small screen can therefore be more analytical and critical – even if they're the same people, on different days.

The effect of this was that I watched the rest of the 1999 World Cup through very different eyes. From this fresh perspective, one couldn't help but realise that South Africa was relying too much on a wagging tail towards the end of their innings in nearly every match of the tournament. In the same way that Jean van de Velde would often be wild off the tee a few weeks later – only to hit some tremendous recovery shots followed by magnificent putts – the Proteas were getting into a habit of making their matches more exciting than they needed to be by getting into early trouble, yet managing to escape unhurt on each occasion.

The South Africans' fourth match, against Kenya, happened to be the one exception. Kenya is better known as the gateway to Kilimanjaro, Africa's highest mountain peak, than it is as a towering strength in the world of international cricket. Much like Amstelveen – the Dutch town on the outskirts of Amsterdam where the Proteas' match against Kenya took place – is known for a river and a beer of the same name, rather than for its importance as a cricket centre.

In the event, Kenya found the match against their fellow Africans rather a tough mountain to climb and one of which they would never quite manage to reach the summit. Lance Klusener collected his third consecutive Man of the Match award, this time for bowling figures of 5 for 21 in 8.3 overs. On the only other occasion that a South African team had played at the ground, Klusener was called upon to open the batting against Holland – only to be dismissed for a single. Memory erased. Roll on Zimbabwe.

By the time the fifth and final round of group matches started, South Africa topped the tables; a place in the Super Six phase of the

'... and nothing but the truth'?

competition was already ensured. They therefore did not have to win the last of their preliminary matches, against Zimbabwe at Chelmsford …

From a Zimbabwean perspective, the match was not a matter of life and death. It was a lot more important than that. They simply had to win if they wanted to progress to the Super Six phase of the tournament. Of further significance was the fact that England also had a very real interest in the match. If Zimbabwe lost, England was ensured of a place in the Super Sixes. If Zimbabwe won, however, England would have to beat India in a match which started on the same day but ended more than twenty-four hours later because of rain delays.

Before the tournament started, Zimbabwe's opening batsman Neil Johnson had played more cricket with members of the South African squad than with any of his Zimbabwean team mates. In the match against the Proteas, he put his knowledge of the opposition's bowling to very good use and scored a match-winning 76. He followed this with some very tight bowling, including the dismissal of Gary Kirsten with the first ball of the South African innings. He also bowled out Hansie Cronjé after the South African captain had executed exactly one scoring shot.

With the Proteas soon at 40 for 6, not even Lance Klusener would be able to rescue them on the day. Zulu eventually ran out of batting partners on 52 not out; South Africa were comprehensively beaten by 48 runs. Zimbabwe had achieved the 'impossible', defeating their southern neighbours for the first time ever in a one-day cricket international. This was quite an achievement for a team of essentially part-timers; people like chicken farmer and medium-pace bowler Eddo Brandes who once said that he'd taken 50 wickets for Zimbabwe and he also had 100,000 chickens; if you asked him about his ambitions, it would be to have 200,000 chickens.

England, meanwhile, orchestrated a batting collapse of note against India and would have to go home with their tail between their legs, had they not been at home already. Worse than this, for another three weeks, the English would have to keep a stiff upper lip and play the role of generous hosts to the teams and supporters of six countries to which they had once exported the game: two from the subcontinent, two from down under, and two from Africa, of all places.

Ask anybody about the two strangest results of the 1999 World Cup and chances are you'll get the same answer: South Africa's loss to

Zimbabwe (which, according to some English supporters, was the 'only' reason why their team was eliminated from the competition), and of course the landslide victory of Bangladesh over Pakistan. A year later, with everything that's since transpired around the world in terms of match-fixing and betting activities, these two outcomes appear even more questionable.

Be that as it may, the two losing teams in question were next to meet in the first match both of them would play in the Super Six round. South Africa were firm favourites, having beaten Pakistan in all of their twelve previous one-day international encounters. The Proteas eventually managed to deliver on that promise, but not before some more heroics from – hold your breath – Lance Klusener. Zulu scored an unbeaten 46 runs from 41 balls, collecting yet another Man of the Match award in the process.

Some interesting things happened during this match. Inzamam-ul-Haq added to his lethargic reputation and was run out by the South Africans for the third time in three consecutive World Cup tournaments. Shoaib Akhtar bowled one of the fastest balls of the tournament at 95 miles per hour. And Hansie Cronjé promoted himself to the number three position in the South African batting line-up for the first time in more than 50 one-day internationals over a period of 26 months.

Cronjé walked to the wicket in the second over of the innings with the South African score at 7/1. An overawed Herschelle Gibbs had just managed to make contact with a ball from Akhtar for the first time, only to push it into the waiting hands of Ijaz at backward point. After scratching around for 10 balls and surviving a confident appeal for caught behind off a short ball, the South African captain eventually managed to play an agricultural shot through the covers for four, his feet nowhere near the ball. A few balls later, Cronjé edged Akhtar high over the slips to be caught on the third man boundary – dismissed for 4 off 15 balls.

The reason why Cronjé decided to promote himself up the order remains unclear to this day. Throughout his career, he was never quite comfortable against really fast bowling, and he was particularly vulnerable against a quality short ball. Add to this not only the fact that he was experiencing his worst run of form ever, but also that he walked in to bat against the fastest bowler in the world ... who had just tasted blood in his first over of the match.

South Africa's next match was against rugby arch-enemies New Zealand. Once again the Proteas were firm favourites, and once again they did not disappoint. Perhaps the most notable incident of the match was that Lance Klusener was dismissed for the first time in the World Cup: bowled for 4. So at last he could say that he had a tournament average: 214, equal to the total number of runs he had acquired over six innings. Including four innings before the World Cup, Klusener had actually scored a total of exactly 400 runs in between dismissals, a new world record.

For once, Hansie Cronjé had a decent match. He scored 39 runs off 22 balls, hitting 2 fours and 2 sixes in the process. He also took 2 wickets for 37 runs in 7 overs. All in all a rather satisfactory day at the office.

One more Super Six match remained for South Africa. Based on the points they'd collected over the course of the competition, they were, however, already sure of a place in the semi-final. Put differently, they did not *have* to beat Australia at Headingley on the 13th of June 1999 …

People often say that an inconsequential match like this is purely of academic interest. Which, if the truth be told, actually means that it is of no interest at all. It was the day that I came to this realisation that I finally decided to quit a career in academia and got myself a job in the business world.

From an Australian perspective it was, however, of much more than academic interest. If they lost, they would pack their bags and watch the knockout stages on television. In this case, the one semi-final would be between South Africa and Zimbabwe, and the other between Pakistan and New Zealand.

So perhaps it wasn't that unimportant for South Africa either – surely a second crack at Zimbabwe would be easier than to play Australia again? In any case, Australia *had* to win whilst South Africa, at best, only *wanted* to win.

The rest is history. In a thrilling match, Herschelle Gibbs first scored a century on the way to helping South Africa to a decent total of 271, only to undo a lot of his own good work by dropping Steve Waugh with the Australian captain's score on 56. Having actually caught the ball, Gibbs attempted to fling it away so quickly that he promptly lost control of it; Waugh went on to score an unbeaten century of his own and fully deserved the Man of the Match award, having secured a victory for his team with two balls to spare. In what will go down as one of the most famous examples of sledging on a cricket pitch ever, Waugh was reported to have said to Gibbs straight after the dropped catch, 'How does it feel to drop the World Cup, Herschelle?'

This is the concise version of what had transpired. Upon closer inspection however, some other decisions and incidents can also be questioned from a South African perspective.

For example, why was Nicky Bojé selected in the place of the injured Jacques Kallis? Many believe that Alan Dawson should have been given a chance – this was after all clearly a seamers' wicket, and it wasn't as if Bojé had settled into the team by then. Steve Waugh promptly hit Bojé out of the attack that day, the spin bowler eventually conceding 29 runs in the only 3 overs he bowled without taking a wicket.

There is perhaps an argument that Bojé should have played in the place of an out-of-form batsman such as Cronjé in addition to Dawson at Headingley, but certainly not instead of the seamer. Indeed in this match, Cronjé attempted to hit the third delivery he faced, from Shane Warne, out of the park with a slog sweep and was trapped leg before wicket. It is interesting to note that up to that ball, Warne had bowled comparatively poorly in the tournament. From that moment on, however, he essentially became the tournament winner.

When it comes to questions regarding pitches and team selection, it should of course be considered against the background of Hansie Cronjé's superior knowledge of the game, as confirmed by coaches and players alike.

Furthermore, Herschelle Gibbs's dropped catch was not the only fielding incident that South Africa may rue for years to come. With Waugh having just reached his century, the batsman got a top edge to long leg. Lance Klusener, whose catch it should have been, for once seemed to make an error of judgement and left the chance to a running Mark Boucher who ended up getting nowhere near the ball. Five overs later, Waugh once again appeared to be fortunate when he lofted the ball in Hansie Cronjé's direction – instead of going for the catch, the South African captain retreated, rather trying to make sure that additional runs be prevented.

Alas. It's no use crying over spilt milk. Australia had won and would face South Africa again in the one semi-final, with Pakistan and New Zealand meeting in the other. Zimbabwe's high hopes had evaporated;

they had to go home to a country facing political strife and economic hardship. Perhaps cricket is, after all, not that important.

There is a compelling argument that Australia should never have reached the knockout stage of the 1999 World Cup. In the preliminary round they lost to Pakistan and were comprehensively beaten by New Zealand; their only victories came against brave Scotland, lowly Bangladesh and an out-of-form West Indies. But they won when it mattered, and now South Africa had their second chance in four days to send the Aussies packing.

At a pre-match press conference, Hansie Cronjé made the following statement:

> I believe there is going to be a lot more drama and excitement to this match than there was in the Super Six encounter at Headingley. On that occasion one team was playing for a semi-final place. Now both teams will be playing for a place in the final. The stakes are much bigger.

And how right wasn't the South African captain eventually proven. Cronjé continued:

> When we started planning the season back in September, I told the guys that there would be a time when they would all have to stand up and accept accountability for their actions. That moment has arrived now.

But, once again, the moment proved too big for the South Africans. The match was a see-saw affair, the initiative changing hands a number of times. When Lance Klusener eventually walked to the wicket, South Africa still needed 39 runs to win off 31 balls. The phlegmatic all-rounder appeared calm as ever on his way to scoring an unbeaten 31 off 16 balls. Meanwhile, in a pub six thousand miles away, a hundred of my closest friends and I were devouring our nails one by one.

With the scores tied and South Africa needing only one run from four balls, Allan Donald seemed intent on running himself out. He managed to do so one ball later. Australia advanced to the final by virtue of a superior run rate in the tournament, 0.19 better than that of the Proteas.

Nominate the South African team for the Darwin awards.

There are many questions about the semi-final match at Edgbaston that remain unanswered to this day.

In the first place, there is the question of why Cronjé elected to bowl after winning the toss. This decision did not seem logical when the world's best wrist spinner would have the benefit of a wearing wicket in the afternoon; Steve Waugh himself said that he would have batted had he won the toss. When Hansie Cronjé won the toss there one week earlier in the Super Six game against New Zealand, he elected to bat. South Africa went on to win by 74 runs that day. Two other World Cup matches were played at Edgbaston: in the first one, a warm-up match between county team Warwickshire and Zimbabwe (who would eventually end up beating South Africa, remember?). Warwickshire batted first and won by 65 runs. In the other one, India beat England by 63 runs after batting first.

Three pretty comprehensive results at the same ground in the month before the semi-final make for a pretty compelling statistic. Why did Cronjé not play the probabilities in arguably the most important match that his country has ever been involved in?

If only it stopped there. An equally strange decision was when Cronjé took himself off after bowling only one tight over for 2 runs in the 41st over of that match. He immediately brought back a tired Steve Elworthy who had already battled through 8 overs for 43 runs without taking a wicket. Elworthy promptly conceded no less than 8 runs in each of his last two overs; Cronjé himself never bowled again on the day.

Then there are persisting questions about South Africa's batting order in the semi-final. Firstly: why was Lance Klusener, Man of the Series and someone who by now had proven himself to be his country's most effective weapon in the last fifteen overs, held back until the end of over number 45? A clear pattern had emerged over the course of the World Cup: Klusener was sent in to bat as soon as the first wicket fell after the commencement of the final 15 overs. The only exceptions to this occurred in the first match against India (when it was obviously still unknown that Klusener was going to be such a force with the bat over the course of the tournament) and on two occasions where Klusener actually went to the crease even earlier, simply because enough wickets had fallen so quickly that Klusener entered the fray in his 'rightful' position at number nine.

In terms of the pattern that had been established, Klusener had gone into bat in positions as varied as number three, six, seven and eight earlier in the tournament – every time as soon as the first wicket fell in the final 15 overs. Yet on that fateful day, when South Africa failed to win the make-or-break game against Australia, the captain elected to break the 'rule' and rather send Shaun Pollock in to bat when the fifth wicket fell in the 41st over. Who knows what might have happened if Lance Klusener was given four more overs to knock off the required runs?

Another issue in respect of the batting order relates to the deployment of Daryll Cullinan at number three in both of the matches against Australia which was a decision publicly criticised by Kepler Wessels and many other commentators.

In South Africa's first seven matches of the tournament, Cullinan was sent in at number five on five occasions and at number four in the other two matches. In all but one of these instances, he went in to bat after Jacques Kallis. Why then send him in to bat in a non-customary position against the team of Shane Warne, Cullinan's long-time bogeyman? In fact, Cullinan's record against the Australians was so poor that he was reportedly not even sure of his place in the side at that stage.

In the first of the two matches against Australia, one can possibly still forgive the captain for his decision to send Daryll Cullinan in when the first wicket fell. Kallis was injured that day and, as mentioned before, it was not a spinners' wicket; theoretically Warne should not have been much of a factor. In spite of this, however, Warne troubled Cullinan no end. He nearly got the batsman with his first ball (a full toss), only conceded 13 runs in the 32 balls that he bowled to Cullinan, and eventually dismissed him with a beautiful delivery.

But in the semi-final there was no excuse for sending in a lamb called Cullinan to the slaughter at number three. Kallis was fit and Warne was in full cry. He had just bowled Herschelle Gibbs with a ball that had spun so much that the batsman did not want to walk, seemingly refusing to believe that he had actually been bowled. After a decent start in which South Africa had accumulated 48 runs in 12 overs before losing their first wicket, the decision to send in an out-of-depth Cullinan at the wrong time stunted the momentum of the whole innings. In the next 9 overs for example, 3 more wickets fell while only 13 runs were added.

In fairness to Hansie Cronjé who came and went during this period, camera replays have shown that his second ball duck (caught in the slips, off Shane Warne, who else?) was one of the worst decisions of the tournament. The ball clearly came off his foot.

Are all these questions merely sour grapes on the part of a disenchanted South African fan; a notoriously bad loser? Perhaps. But one cannot help wondering about some of the mysteries of those two matches between South Africa and Australia. One cannot help thinking about what might have been.

It just never needed to be that close.

In closing, an opinion about the apportionment of blame between Lance Klusener and Allan Donald for that final run-out.

Call me a fence-sitter, but I don't think either of them should take the flack. Lance Klusener did the right thing by running as the ball was hit in front of the wicket; in terms of first principles it was his call. Allan Donald did the right thing by going back as the ball could have hit the wickets at the non-strikers end. In terms of first principles, his primary responsibility was to make sure that he didn't get run out on that side.

Add to this the cacophony of sound around the ground and the tremendous tension of the occasion, and it's easy to understand why the calling between the two went awry. These things happen.

How can you blame a batsman who had just scored 31 runs off 16 balls in nerve-wracking circumstances, not to mention the other 250 runs he

South Africa	1st match	2nd match	Total runs
G Kirsten	21	18	39
H Gibbs	101	30	131
D Cullinan	50	6	56
J Kallis	DNP	53	53
H Cronjé	0	0	0
J Rhodes	39	43	82
L Klusener	36	31	67
S Pollock	3	20	23
M Boucher	0	5	5
S Elworthy	DNB	1	1
A Donald	DNB	0	0
Extras	21	6	27
TOTAL	**271**	**213**	

scored at an overall strike rate of more than 1.2 per ball over the course of the tournament? And how can you even think of blaming his partner, the number eleven batsman who earlier in the day finished with the astonishing bowling figures of 4 for 32 off 10 overs? Surely it shouldn't be his job to score the winning runs as well?

If any specialist batsman had just scored one more run earlier in the day, that would have been all that was required …

In order to shed further light on the topic, the table below provides a player-by-player comparison of the South African and Australian batting performances over the course of the two matches they played against each other during the 1999 World Cup.

The table underlines the marvellous achievements of Herschelle Gibbs, Jacques Kallis and Lance Klusener of beating their Australian counterparts hands down. Even Gary Kirsten, who didn't have two great knocks, managed to outscore an out-of-sorts Mark Waugh quite comfortably. And Jonty Rhodes was only narrowly beaten by Michael Bevan, but both batsmen could hold their heads high in a closely fought duel. Even the South African tail ended with positive numbers.

This leaves Daryll Cullinan versus Ricky Ponting at number three, and the battle of the captains, Hansie Cronjé versus Steve Waugh.

Should Cullinan ever have been selected against Australia? And what if Hansie Cronjé didn't go out for a duck in both of the matches against them?

Australia	1st match	2nd match	Total runs	Differential: SA minus Australia
M Waugh	5	0	5	34
A Gilchrist	5	20	25	106
R Ponting	69	37	106	(50)
Martyn/Lehmann	11	1	12	41
S Waugh	120	56	176	(176)
M Bevan	27	65	92	(10)
T Moody	15	0	15	52
S Warne	DNB	18	18	5
P Reiffel	DNB	0	0	5
D Fleming	DNB	0	0	1
G McGrath	DNB	0	0	0
Extras	20	16	36	(9)
	272	213		

6

What do the statistics say?

You get lies, damned lies … and then you get statistics.

Any student of the subject will tell you that there are numerous potential pitfalls when performing statistical analysis. One should, for example, always question the assumptions on which an analysis is based. Are they realistic and fair? Or were they made to suit a desired outcome? And, when performing the analysis, are there reasonable grounds for the inclusion or exclusion of any specific data item?

Data mining is another demon that sometimes rears its head. This basically means that the analyst tries numerous different angles in the hope that one of the tests will throw out something significant. A university professor of mine once referred to this as 'torturing the data until it confesses'; a very appropriate description.

A statistician further needs to ensure that there's a sufficiently large universe of information with which to work. To analyse the ways that a relatively new international batsman such as Andrew Hall has been dismissed would be near meaningless, but any statistician with a passion for cricket would rub his hands in glee at the prospect of analysing the record of an established player such as Steve Waugh.

No South African player has played nearly as many matches as Waugh with his 130-odd test matches and 300 one-day internationals. What then is considered to be an appropriate number of matches in order for analysis to be meaningful? How long is a piece of string? There is no real answer, but one can argue that 100 innings or more by

141

a batsman is sufficient for certain basic trends to establish themselves.

Finally, there is the issue of causality. A strong relationship between two sets of numbers (formally referred to as one that is statistically significant) does not necessarily imply that either one actually influences the other. Does X cause Y, or vice versa? Or is any relationship between them purely coincidental?

A famous example in this regard – from the business world – is the often quoted relationship between the level of ladies' hemlines and share price performance in the American stock market. Over the last 100 years it can be proven that there is a very strong statistical relationship between the two variables, but readers are likely to agree that nobody can really argue with conviction how changes in either one should actually affect the other.

The rather entertaining hemline example has been used to emphasise that the graphs and tables that follow do not actually *prove* anything. The intention is merely to point out certain interesting facts and to ask a few questions. Some answers may take many years to crystallise; others may forever be shrouded in mystery.

The beauty of cricket is that there are so many numbers and variables to analyse. Just compare it to a simple game such as rugby. All rugby players stop scoring points in any given match for one of two reasons: either the match ends, or they leave the field because of injury or replacement. In cricket, a batsman may obviously be forced to stop scoring runs for similar reasons. In addition to that, however, his stay at the crease may also be terminated in at least seven other ways. In rugby, when you get the ball you always try and do something with it as quickly as possible (whether running, passing or kicking). In cricket, on the other hand, there is a whole spectrum of respectable speeds at which a ball may be bowled. Imagine a rugby player who describes himself as 'slow' or 'medium fast' seeking selection as a specialist at representative level! Or try and convince the captain of a rugby team that he should 'declare' before the final whistle because his team is considered to have adequate points on the board!

Perhaps that is why cricket matches (even the one-day variety) last so much longer than most other sports events. It's self-evident, really – there's just so much more to think about in cricket; so many subtle variations to savour. Seldom is this point so clearly made as when a fiercely competitive five-day test match ends in a draw and spectators or commentators agree that it was an excellent match. Five days? No result? Excellent? You must be joking! What boggles the mind of the layman sometimes makes perfect sense to the connoisseur.

The statistical angle to the game of cricket is also a wonderful leveller amongst spectators. At a rugby match, it will often add credence to your opinions in the pavilion if you're built like an international lock forward. In cricket, however, your physique won't help you one bit if the required run rate needs to be calculated quickly (to a specified number of decimals). I still remember a misspent youth, sitting to the left of what is now the Centenary Pavilion at the Wanderers stadium for days on end, trying to match a friend of a friend at calculating all sorts of ratios (an area in which I would normally quite fancy myself). He beat me hands down every time, and I could only take comfort in the fact that he was three years older than me. And he was seriously bright: he eventually went to America where he qualified as a rocket scientist or a brain surgeon (there was, however, no way that he could actually swing a cricket bat himself).

So what questions relating to the Hansie Cronjé saga might one ask of a statistician?

As a specialist batsman, an obvious one to start with would be to analyse how his batting average might be different when looking at the periods before and after his first documented introduction to members of the betting community. Is there any significant trend in form when comparing one period to another?

What then should be the cut-off point before and after which averages are compared? In Hansie Cronjé's comprehensive statement to the King Commission on 15 June 2000, he mentions that he was first approached by bookies at the time of the Mandela Trophy tournament in South Africa (December 1994 – January 1995). Cronjé does of course not admit to any form of match-fixing on his part, either during this tournament or at any other time, resulting in a conclusion that there is probably no single date which is better to focus on than this one.

There is another very good reason why the time of the Mandela Trophy is significant, and that is because it coincides with Cronjé's official appointment as captain of the South African national team. Before that, he captained his country on seven occasions in one-day internationals as well as one test match, when Kepler Wessels was injured (all of these in Australia, in January 1994). Wessels did, however, return as captain for six tests and sixteen one-day internationals during the rest of 1994.

Curiously, Cronjé seems to create a different impression in the very first paragraph of his statement to the King Commission when he says, 'I captained the South African team from the third test of the Australian series in 1994 until 11 April 2000.' Technically this may be right, for that third test against the Australians was indeed the first instance of his captaincy, but the way that he formulates it seems to suggest that he was captain over the full period (not allowing for Wessels's return for the remainder of 1994).

Why would Hansie do this? Could it be an attempt to put some distance between his actual appointment as captain and his first, self-confessed 'involvement' with bookies, when indeed there was none? Whether he wanted to or not, Cronjé could not start his references to any sort of interaction with the betting community at any *later* date than that. The reason for this is that Pat Symcox had mentioned the Mandela Trophy incident in his own testimony before Cronjé took the stand (although of course Symcox got the actual date of the Mandela Trophy wrong when he testified).

If one accepts that there are international betting syndicates actively at work in cricket, it stands to reason that the most obvious players who would be approached are the captains of the various teams. Given the amounts that are allegedly involved, as well as the persistent nature of such activities, it also stands to reason that a new captain is quite likely to receive his first approach soon after being appointed. It is obviously easier for the outcome of a cricket match to be influenced when a few players collude than when one person tries by himself ... and who better than the captain to play a facilitating role in this regard?

In his benefit publication, *Hansie: This is your captain speaking*, Hansie Cronjé himself stresses the importance of a captain's influence on a game of cricket, as follows.

> **No single player can ever be blamed for losing a game, though**
> **the captain comes closest to this. It is he who orchestrates the**

team's strategy on the field, and he often has to make crucial and pivotal decisions in the space of a few minutes on which the outcome of the game might turn.

The date of Hansie Cronjé's official appointment as the South African captain will thus be the main focus of the analysis that follows. As his appointment coincided with the start of the Mandela Trophy, I will for the sake of simplicity refer to the pre-Mandela and post-Mandela eras in Cronjé's cricket career. This, of course, is not to be confused with similar terminology which is often used in a political context in South Africa!

*   *   *   *   *

Figure 1 illustrates the development of Hansie Cronjé's career average in one-day internationals. No dramatic trend is evident in the latter stages of his career, partly because every additional innings will at that stage, by definition, have comparatively little additional impact on the overall average (as each new score continues to be added on to an ever-increasing base).

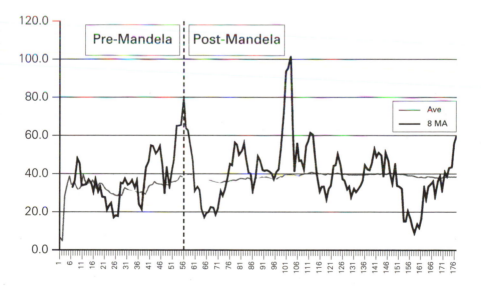

Figure 1 – Hansie Cronjé: overall batting average and 8-innings moving average (one-day international career)

Figure 1 does, however, also show an 8-innings moving average for Cronjé which requires some further explanation. Most cricket enthusiasts will be quite familiar with the concept of a player's batting average: you simply divide the total runs scored by the number of times the batsman was dismissed over the period. The reason for excluding the times that the batsman was not dismissed from the denominator, is that the batsman is given the benefit of the doubt: who knows how many additional runs he might have scored if the innings did not end when it did?

This slight quirk in the way that batting averages are calculated does of course sometimes lead to strange situations. Remember Lance Klusener's amazing run of form in the 1999 World Cup in England? In his first five innings he scored 12, 52, 48, 52 and 46 – *all not out!* This not only meant that he didn't actually have an official tournament average at that stage (as you cannot divide by zero), it also meant that his average would be 210 (the total of these five scores) if he went out for a duck the next time he went in to bat. Klusener eventually ended the World Cup with an average of 140.5, having been dismissed only twice in eight innings – easily justifying his award as player of the tournament. The fact that he could have an average amounting to more than two and a half times his highest score could certainly confuse any non-cricketing mathematician!

One final point about the Klusener streak: in his last four innings in one-day internationals immediately before the World Cup, as well as the first two after that tournament, he scored a total of 294 runs without being dismissed once. His average for that run of fourteen consecutive innings thus amounted to no less than 252 (highest score over the period: 103 not out against New Zealand in New Zealand, his best ever score in a one-day international at the time of writing this book).

The 8-innings moving average as shown in Figure 1 takes the concept of the batting average one step further by focusing on the batsman's form over the eight most recent times that he went in to bat (adjusting for not outs in the same way as described above). The first few innings of a batsman will thus eventually be excluded from any such moving average statistic (although they will always be included in his overall average). It follows that any shorter-term moving average measure will always be significantly more volatile than an overall average.

Why focus on an 8-innings moving average (and not, for example, 6

146

innings or 15 innings)? These questions can indeed be asked and there is no firm answer either way. If one were, in fact, to use these numbers, similar trends would emerge – only with a bit more volatility in the case of a 6-innings moving average, and less volatility in the case of a 15-innings moving average. A number of 8 is considered meaningful as it approximates the length of a typical one-day series (World Cup or otherwise); it is also a high enough number to be meaningful and short enough that the smoothing effect, as discussed, should not be too extreme.

Figure 1 clearly shows how Cronjé's 8-innings moving average starts declining sharply from a level in the upper 60s at the beginning of the post-Mandela period, to a low of 17.3 some ten matches later. Notably, the 8-innings moving average picks up again to reach an all-time high in excess of 100 after another forty matches. This sharp increase is due, in part, to a period where Cronjé scored a total of 264 runs in six innings and being dismissed only once in the process (three of these innings were against Zimbabwe at the beginning of 1997).

Can Cronjé's sudden decline in form at the beginning of the post-Mandela era simply be explained in terms of the additional pressures of captaincy?

What is further evident from Figure 1 (and specifically the 8-innings moving average), is the poor form that Cronjé experienced from about the time of the tour to New Zealand in February 1999 until just after the end of that year's World Cup (i.e. from innings number 144 to innings number 157). Over this period, his 8-innings moving average drops from approximately 50 to below 10.

The 1999 World Cup was arguably the worst run of form ever experienced by Cronjé. With a tournament average of a mere 12.3 in eight innings, the only two members of the squad faring worse were pace bowlers Allan Donald and Steve Elworthy. So much has been made of that dramatic last-ball confusion when Donald was run out in the semi-final against Australia. But how different might the outcome have been if Cronjé, a top-order batsman, did not score a duck in both of those last two matches against the Aussies?

Returning to Figure 1, it should be noted that Cronjé's 8-innings moving average picks up again sharply in his last twenty one-day internationals to end at a level just slightly below 60. On reflection, it seems rather ironic that these last eight innings were, in fact, all against teams from the subcontinent: the first five against India (in India) and the last three against Pakistan and India (in Sharjah).

More specifically, the Indian tour referred to was the same one where Cronjé experienced 'incessant nagging' by bookmakers (according to his own statement before the King Commission), and where he ended up approaching Pieter Strydom, Jacques Kallis, Mark Boucher, Lance Klusener, Herschelle Gibbs and Henry Williams in the context of possible match-fixing. Cronjé himself scored fifties in three of those last eight innings, going out in a blaze of glory with 79 off only 73 balls in his last match for South Africa – the Coca-Cola Cup final against Pakistan in Sharjah on the 31st of March 2000.

* * * * *

When one progresses the analysis of Hansie Cronjé's form on the sub-continent a bit further, an interesting picture emerges. (For the purpose of this analysis, the subcontinent is defined as India, Pakistan, Sri Lanka, Bangladesh and the United Arab Emirates.)

It can be argued that Cronjé opens himself up to this kind of scrutiny when he approaches the end of his statement before the King

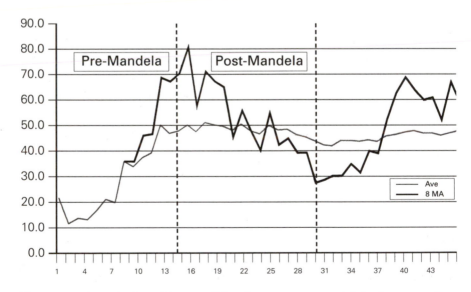

Figure 2 – Hansie Cronjé: overall batting average and 8-innings moving average (one-day international career – matches on subcontinent only)

148

Commission by saying: 'I think a serious effort should be made to educate and warn players – *particularly before tours to the subcontinent* – of the dangers posed by sports betting and gamblers' (author's emphasis).

It's certainly interesting to note not only how quickly Cronjé's form drops after the beginning of the post-Mandela period, but also how consistent this trend is over approximately the next 15 matches (starting with the World Cup at the beginning of 1996, and finishing with the end of the Titan Cup tournament in India at the end of that year). As Figure 2 clearly illustrates, Cronjé's 8-innings moving average drops from a level of over 80 to under 30 over this period.

A few points should be made about the severe slump in Cronjé's form on the subcontinent at the beginning of the post-Mandela era. Firstly, one can argue that this was in spite of the batting conditions on the subcontinent actually suiting him. There is ample support for this. To start with, his career average in subcontinental one-day internationals was nearly 50 (as shown in Figure 2), significantly more than his overall international average at that stage of 38.6 (as shown in Figure 1). In fact, when one strips all Cronjé's innings on the subcontinent out of his overall record, his average in all one-day internationals *outside* the subcontinent drops to only 35.3.

Part of the reason why the subcontinent suited Cronjé well, is the fact that he was always very good against spin-bowling. It is a well-known fact that a lot of pitches in this area ideally suit the spinners, which often leads to more of them being included per team than anywhere else in the world.

Cronjé regularly proved his mettle against quality spin-bowling, not only on the subcontinent, but also against Shane Warne, arguably the greatest spinner of the ball of all time. Where Daryll Cullinan would falter, Hansie Cronjé would often flourish. In eight one-day internationals between South Africa and Australia at the beginning of 1994, for example (when Warne was generally considered to be at or near his best), Cronjé averaged no less than 55 and often hit Warne out of the bowling attack.

It follows that Cronjé's ability to play spin would increase his 'market value' to bookies on the subcontinent, increasing the chances that he would be targeted by them. It's obvious that there's more money to be made by 'buying' the wicket of someone who had an above-average probability of making a decent score on any given day (conversely, it would seem pointless to buy the wicket of a poor batsman).

Returning to Figure 2, the timing of the end of Cronjé's severe slump in form on the subcontinent in the post-Mandela era (as indicated by the second vertical line inserted on the graph) is perhaps of even more significance. The reason for this is that the timing of the start of his return to form coincides with the now-famous meeting where he discussed the possibility of 'throwing' the final one-day international of the 1996 Indian tour with the team. One can only speculate about the possibility that Cronjé might have been so put out when he did not get support from his team-mates for the proposal, that he therefore tried even harder to prove his bona fides to all concerned in the period that followed.

* * * * *

The previous analysis concentrated only on the one-day internationals in which Cronjé played. When shifting the focus to his test career, a slightly different picture emerges. Before comparing graphs of the two, one point does, however, need to be clarified.

The time line of a test batting career is very different to that of a one-day international career. One-day internationals are a lot more straightforward: a top-order batsman will bat once in nearly every match he plays in (Cronjé batted 175 times in 188 matches he played in, or 93% of the time).

Tests are different as more subtleties are introduced, inter alia by the concept of a second innings (which of course falls away in the case of an innings victory). Cronjé, for example, batted 111 times in the 68 tests in which he played (i.e. he had a second innings only approximately 80% of the time).

There is, of course, rather an ironic twist in the fact that Hansie Cronjé's test career ended after exactly 111 test innings. Cricket enthusiasts in most parts of the world will be familiar with the concept of the 'Nelson' – a superstition in terms of which 111 is considered to be a 'dangerous' score for a batsman (or for a team). When wickets are lost on this total, commentators will often make a meal of it. In Australia there is a similar superstition, although it applies to a different score – in that country, 87 is considered to be dangerous (an unlucky 13 away from 100).

Not only players and/or commentators believe in Nelson. One of the concept's most famous proponents is leading international umpire, David Shepherd from England, who has officiated in more than 50 test matches. He also stood in the finals of the last two World Cups and was awarded an MBE for services to cricket in 1997. Umpire Shepherd is well known for the fact that he stands on one leg whenever the score reaches not only the Nelson level, but also that of double and triple Nelson (222, 333 etc).

When viewing Hansie Cronjé's record over his 111 test innings in Figure 3, it is interesting to note that his run of form (as depicted again by the 8-innings moving average) seems quite different from that of his one-day international career. Instead of the moving average falling at the beginning of the post-Mandela era (as was evident in the case of Cronjé's one-day international career), it actually starts by rising sharply in his first eleven innings. This can possibly be ascribed to the quality of the opposition over that period, as nine of the eleven innings were against New Zealand and Zimbabwe respectively (which was not the case in his first ten or so one-day internationals over the same period).

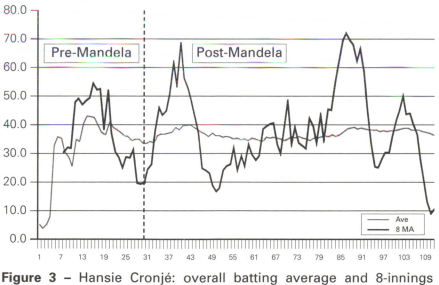

Figure 3 – Hansie Cronjé: overall batting average and 8-innings moving average (test match career)

Figure 3 does, however, also show how Cronjé's form slumped soon after those first few innings against New Zealand and Zimbabwe at the beginning of the post-Mandela era. This was most pronounced over a period of approximately 15 months from the end of 1995 to the beginning of 1997 in series against England, India and Australia. During this time, Cronjé had twelve innings at an average of only 24.3 specifically against India.

A final point: when comparing Cronjé's form in one-day internationals to that in test matches in the latter part of his career, it would appear that his test form was declining at the same time that his one-day form was starting to pick up again. This can once more be ascribed, at least in part, to different time lines: over the same period that Cronjé played his last nine innings in one-day internationals (all on the subcontinent), he only batted three times in test matches.

$$* \quad * \quad * \quad * \quad *$$

When contemplating the possible impact of any involvement with book-makers on a batsman's form over time, another interesting point would be to analyse how he went out over the course of his career. Considering the different ways in which a batsman can be dismissed, it appears obvious that being caught out is the one which can most easily be associated with reckless behaviour.

Thinking back over the career of Hansie Cronjé, one cannot help but recall many a splendid shot sailing over the wide mid-wicket boundary. One is, however, also reminded of how many times he was caught out in the same area. This often led to criticism in the press that he should perhaps have been more prudent in executing the famous slog-sweep – and that was *before* anyone suspected him of match-fixing!

In retrospect, a hypothesis of reckless batting may well be put forward in terms of Herschelle Gibbs's performance in the fifth one-day international at Nagpur in March 2000. Much has been made of the fact that he first agreed to lose his wicket for less than 20 runs, but then 'forgot' about the arrangement – going on to score no less than 74 on the day. When one considers that he hit fours off the first

During the now-famous last day of the Centurion test against England, January 2000 – watching the big screen to make sure that Maddy was indeed run out by Kirsten. (Shaun Pollock, Jacques Kallis, Pieter Strydom, Herschelle Gibbs, Daryll Cullinan, Mark Boucher, Hansie Cronjé).

Hansie Cronjé's last public appearance as a cricketer before the betting scandal broke – in the single-wicket competition at Newlands, April 2000.

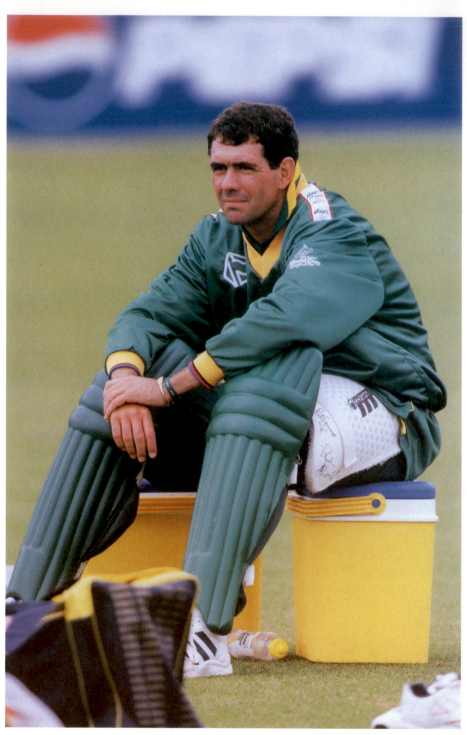

The captain in pensive mood before the World Cup warm-up match against Kent at Canterbury, 9 May 1999. The WWJD band can be seen on his left wrist.

So near but yet so far ... a symbolic picture of the widening rift between coach and captain (before the World Cup warm-up match against Kent at Canterbury, 9 May 1999).

Supporters of Muttiah Muralitharan at the World Cup opening match between England and Sri Lanka at Lord's, 14 May 1999.

Hansie Cronjé with the famous earpiece, World Cup match against India at Hove, 15 May 1999.

Sitting amongst the Indian supporters at Hove – South Africa's first match in the 1999 World Cup.

Before the World Cup match against Sri Lanka, Northampton.

The pressure of captaincy – Hansie Cronjé entertains a multitude of reporters the day before the World Cup match against England at The Oval, 22 May 1999.

Ali Bacher and Marie Gouws under the famous Animated Clock at The Oval.

The 'South African pavilion' at The Oval, 22 May 1999.

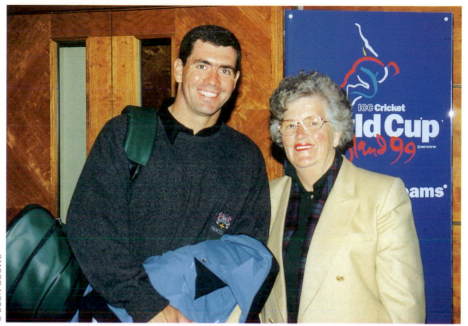

Hansie Cronjé and Marie Gouws, his greatest fan, the morning after South Africa trounced England at The Oval in the 1999 World Cup.

Hansie Cronjé congratulates Gary Kirsten after running out Adam Parore in the Super Six match against New Zealand (Edgbaston, 10 June 1999).

Hansie Cronjé in full cry as a batsman – executing the famous slog-sweep against New Zealand in the Super Six match at Edgbaston, 10 June 1999. In his best match of the tournament, Cronjé scored 39 from 22 balls, including 2 fours and 2 sixes.

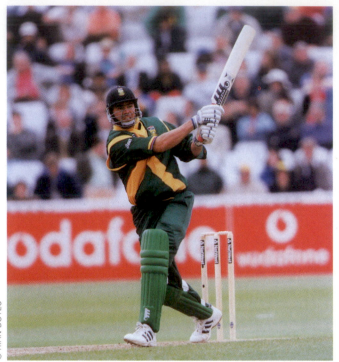

Hansie Cronjé on his way to bowling figures of 2/37 from 7 overs against New Zealand in the Super Six match at Edgbaston, 10 June 1999. Umpire Venkat looks on.

Shane Warne scratches his head during the Super Six match at Headingley, 13 June 1999. Herschelle Gibbs, who scored a brilliant century, had the better of him on the day.

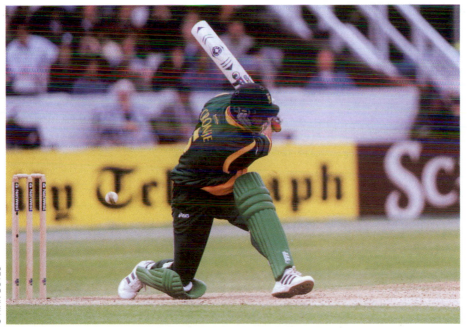

Hansie Cronjé plays across the line and is trapped LBW, third ball against Shane Warne in the Super Six match at Headingley, 13 June 1999.

© RIAN BOTES

Hansie Cronjé and stalwart fast bowler Allan Donald examine the ball in the second last over of the Super Six match against Australia (Headingley, 13 June 1999).

© RIAN BOTES

Herschelle Gibbs speaking on his cellphone in the team bus ... not looking too concerned the day after 'dropping the World Cup for South Africa' (Steve Waugh's words) in the Super Six match against Australia (Headingley, 13 June 1999).

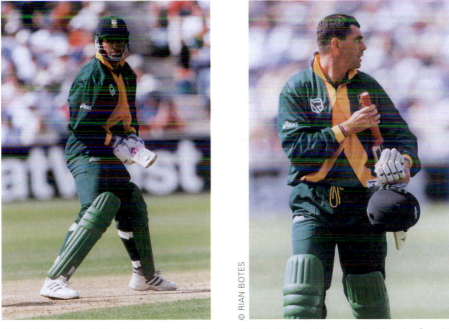

World Cup Semi-Final, Edgbaston, 17 June 1999. Shane Warne gets Hansie Cronjé
– again (Daryll Cullinan is the non-striking batsman). This time second ball, Cronjé
was given out caught in the slips after the ball had struck his foot. Clearly dismayed,
Cronjé watches the dismissal on the big screen on the way to the pavilion.

Dr Ali Bacher, Managing Director of the United Cricket Board of South Africa, testifies before the King Commission at the Centre for the Book, Cape Town.

Judge Edwin King

Advocate Shamila Batohi, the Chief Investigator in the probe into match-fixing allegations.

Ewie Cronjé, Hansie's father, at the King Commission.

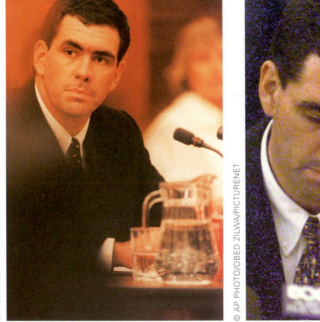

Hansie Cronjé testifies before the King Commission.

© MUJAHIEL SAFODIEN/TRACE IMAGES

© AP PHOTO/OBED ZILWA/PICTURENET

Marlon Aronstam at the King Commission – Aronstam influenced Hansie Cronjé in his decision to forfeit an innings in the final test against England at Centurion, January 2000.

Herschelle Gibbs at the King Commission.

© MUJAHIEL SAFODIEN/TRACE IMAGES

Hamid 'Banjo' Cassim referred to himself as a good friend of Hansie Cronjé's at the King Commission; Cronjé called Cassim a 'hanger-on'.

two balls that he faced, and that he only needed 53 balls to score those 74 runs (hitting 13 fours and a six in the process), the question could well be asked whether or not he was simply throwing bat at ball, 'trying' to get out, but somehow hitting it just wide of the fielders all the time (or over their heads).

In Figure 4 (overleaf), the ways that Cronjé was dismissed over his career are compared with those of other prominent batsman. As opposed to the earlier analysis in this appendix, it should be noted that test matches and one-day internationals are combined in this case (something which can, of course, never be done in the case of batting *averages*).

Note further that catches by the wicketkeeper are distinguished from other catches, as an edge is actually a very different dismissal to being caught out in front of the wicket. If one extends this logic, all catches in the slips should, of course, be added to the wicket-keeper catches, but unfortunately these detailed statistics are not available.

To which batsmen should one compare Cronjé? Firstly, it should be mostly South African players who played in the same era, as they would have all played in similar conditions and against the similar quality bowling to Cronjé. Secondly, one should focus on right-handed players, like Cronjé, as left-handers typically respond quite differently to specific bowlers, for example. Thirdly, one should avoid players who open the batting, as the new ball conditions that apply to them are dissimilar to those experienced by the rest of the top and middle order. And lastly, only those players with a sufficient number of innings should be included in order to make the analysis meaningful.

All things considered, the only three players who thus stand out are Jacques Kallis, Jonty Rhodes and Daryll Cullinan. As this is quite a small number of players, the statistics for two other batsmen are included in Figure 4: Gary Kirsten (a left-handed opener – but he did play in more similar matches to Cronjé than anyone else), and Steve Waugh (an Australian – but the sheer number of innings he has played makes for meaningful averages; there are also some similarities to Cronjé's attacking style of batting, for example).

	H Cronjé	G Kirsten	J Kallis	J Rhodes	D Cullinan	S Waugh
Bowled	39	48	24	29	42	90
LBW	13	22	13	31	16	34
Run out	25	15	11	13	14	18
Stumped	6	7	4	4	8	11
Caught-wk	45	37	28	32	27	83
Caught	118	80	44	82	78	130
Other	0	1	1	0	2	1
Not out	40	22	23	39	21	91
Total	286	232	148	230	208	468

	H Cronjé	G Kirsten	J Kallis	J Rhodes	D Cullinan	S Waugh
Bowled	13.6%	20.7%	16.2%	12.6%	20.2%	19.2%
LBW	4.5%	9.5%	8.8%	13.5%	7.7%	7.3%
Run out	8.7%	6.5%	7.4%	5.7%	6.7%	6.0%
Stumped	2.1%	3.0%	2.7%	1.7%	3.8%	2.4%
Caught-wk	15.7%	15.9%	18.9%	13.9%	13.0%	17.7%
Caught	**41.3%**	**34.5%**	**29.7%**	**35.7%**	**37.5%**	**27.8%**
Other	0.0%	0.4%	0.7%	0.0%	1.0%	0.2%
Not out	14.0%	9.5%	15.5%	17.0%	10.1%	19.4%
Total	100.0%	100.0%	100.0%	100.0%	100.0%	100.0%

Figure 4 – Six prominent batsmen: ways of dismissal over career (test matches and one-day internationals combined, statistics to June 2000)

It is clear from Figure 4 that the percentage of times Cronjé was caught out in his career (41.3% of the time) is higher than any of the other players.

Before one draws any strong conclusions from this, one has to recognise that different players not only have different styles of batting, they simply also have different strengths and weaknesses. Jonty Rhodes, for example, has gone out leg before wicket far more often than any other player included in Figure 4, but anyone who has watched him bat will know that this is due in no small measure to his habit of shuffling in front of his stumps, attempting to pull or sweep the ball (a favourite shot of his).

'... and nothing but the truth'?

Further analysis is thus required. Figure 5 (below) provides a summary of the ways in which Hansie Cronjé was dismissed over his career, distinguishing between the pre-Mandela and post-Mandela periods.

Figure 5 shows that there is indeed a marked difference between the pre-Mandela and post-Mandela eras in Hansie Cronjé's career, with the percentage of times that he is caught out increasing from 32% to no less than 45%.

Interestingly, his pre-Mandela average of 32% seems squarely in the 'right' ball park (the combined average of the other five players in Figure 4 is 33%).

	Pre-Mandela	Post-Mandela	Total
Bowled	19	20	39
LBW	4	9	13
Run out	9	16	25
Stumped	2	4	6
Caught-wk	9	36	45
Caught	27	91	118
Other	0	0	0
Not out	14	26	40
Total	84	202	286

	Pre-Mandela	Post-Mandela	Total
Bowled	22.6%	9.9%	13.6%
LBW	4.8%	4.5%	4.5%
Run out	10.7%	7.9%	8.7%
Stumped	2.4%	2.0%	2.1%
Caught-wk	10.7%	17.8%	15.7%
Caught	**32.1%**	**45%**	**41.3%**
Other	0.0%	0.0%	0.0%
Not out	16.7%	12.9%	14.0%
Total	100%	100%	100%

Figure 5 – Hansie Cronjé: ways of dismissal over career (test matches and one-day internationals combined)

What do the statistics say?

This information can also be summarised in the form of a bar chart as per Figure 6. It clearly illustrates the marked difference between the pre- and post-Mandela periods with reference to the percentage of times that Hansie Cronjé was caught out; and also how this compares to the career statistics of other prominent batsman.

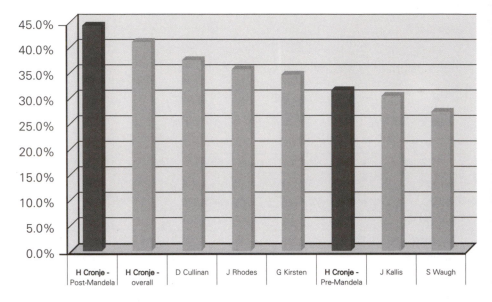

Figure 6 – Six prominent batsmen: percentage of times caught over career (test matches and one-day internationals combined, statistics to June 2000)

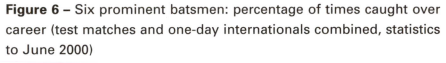

The focus of the analysis up to this point has been exclusively on Hansie Cronjé's batting. It is well known, however, that the ex-South African captain was also a very useful medium-pace bowler, as illustrated by his best bowling figures in a one-day international of 5 for 32 against India in 1992.

Bowling is more difficult to analyse than batting. When a batsman walks to the crease, the intention is basically always the same, namely to score as many runs as possible. In a nutshell, the best batsmen are those who score the most runs over time.

In the case of bowling, however, there are two very different measures of success. Any bowler clearly tries to take as many wickets as possible, whilst conceding as few runs as possible in the process. Which of the two objectives is most important, will often depend on the circumstances (including whether the game in question is a test match or a one-day international).

The concept of a bowler's average is an attempt to combine both of these measures (wickets taken and runs conceded) and combine them into a single statistic. This is done by dividing the total number of runs conceded by the total number of wickets taken. The result is an average which can intuitively be referred to as a bowler's 'cost' per wicket (as measured in runs conceded, on average, for every wicket taken). The great bowlers have averages in the low 20s; Hansie Cronjé's test bowling average was 29.95 and his one-day average was 34.78.

When Hansie Cronjé's batting form was analysed above, it was done with reference to an 8-innings moving average. In terms of a consistent approach, it follows that the same should therefore be done in the case of his bowling average. There is, however, a problem in that there were periods in both Cronjé's test career as well as his one-day international career where he didn't take any wickets for more than eight innings in a row. This results in a situation where it becomes impossible to measure the 8-innings moving average, as one cannot divide by zero (in terms of mathematical principles). Therefore, this kind of analysis can simply not be done as far as Hansie Cronjé's bowling career is concerned.

It should be noted that when referring to prolonged periods where Cronjé failed to take wickets, this does not necessarily imply that he was bowling badly. He may have been bowling quite economically, he was just not taking wickets. This leads to another bowling statistic which is typically measured, namely the economy rate.

To illustrate: it is theoretically possible that a so-called 'strike bowler' can take a relatively large number of wickets and therefore end up with a decent average, in spite of the fact that he may actually have been quite expensive in the process (as measured by the number of runs conceded per over). Specifically in the case of limited-overs matches, it is often as important to prevent the opposition from scoring as it is to take their wickets.

As an example, it is quite conceivable that a bowler with figures of 0 for 15 in 10 overs could have added more to his team's success than someone with figures of 3 for 50 in 10 overs, in the same limited-overs match. Whether or not this is in fact the case may depend on the circumstances (e.g. who were the batsmen dismissed by the second bowler; were they the danger men, etc.) As with so many things in this wonderfully complex game of cricket, there is simply no hard-and-fast rule. It is, however, clear that the second bowler in the example has probably done his overall average more good than bad, whereas the first one's average could only have deteriorated in the process.

It is for this reason that a bowler's economy rate is also an often-quoted statistic. The algebra is simple: one merely divides runs conceded by overs bowled in order to arrive at an 'average runs per over'. Although this measure is considered to be most important in the case of limited-overs matches, there is no reason not to calculate it in the case of tests as well.

Hansie Cronjé's bowling form can thus be analysed over time with reference to an 8-innings moving average economy rate, as depicted in Figure 7. (At the risk of stating the patently obvious, it should be borne in mind that a *lower* bowling economy rate is always preferable to a higher one – compared to a batting average which is always better the *higher* it is).

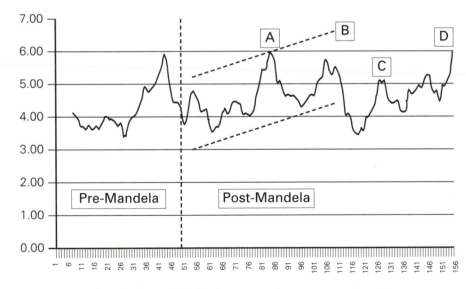

Figure 7 – Hansie Cronjé: 8-innings moving average bowling economy rate (one-day international career)

Figure 7 illustrates how there seems to be a deterioration in Hansie Cronjé's economy rate from innings 50 (the beginning of the post-Mandela period) to innings 83 (identified as point A on the graph). After this, the trend is quite volatile with periods of good and bad form alternating – any conclusions from this are thus likely to be rather tenuous.

It is, however, interesting to note where the matches were played when Hansie Cronjé's form as a bowler was at its worst (as identified by points A, B, C and D in Figure 7). In the case of point A, Cronjé's economy rate happened to be at its worst in the middle of the Titan Cup in India at the end of 1996. In addition to this, of the ten previous innings in which Cronjé turned his arm over (i.e. as the economy rate was rising sharply – refer Figure 7), eight were on the subcontinent (the first four in Sharjah and the last four in India, with two in between in Kenya – although Cronjé bowled a total of only three overs in Kenya)

The three overs in Kenya (spread over two matches in September-October 1996) need some clarification. It should be noted that the impact of these bowling efforts on the 8-innings moving average economy rate will be minimal, simply based on the small number of overs involved. The moving average is in fact a *weighted* average, with longer bowling spells thus having a bigger effect on the average than shorter ones. (This is because the *total* number of runs as well as the *total* number of overs bowled in the last eight innings are used in the calculation.)

Returning to Cronjé's poor bowling form as identified by point A in Figure 7, the Titan Cup in India was part of the tour that ended with the Mohinder Amarnath Benefit Match on the 14th of December 1996. This was the match before which Hansie Cronjé put the $250,000 to the team in an incident which has since received so much publicity.

Another very interesting thing happened in the match following immediately after the one referred to as point A in Figure 7. Hansie Cronjé brought himself on to bowl during that next match, but only for one over which yielded two runs.

Why did he stop bowling after one over, one should ask, and a very economical over at that? Only twice in Hansie Cronjé's one-day international career did he remove himself after a first over in which two or less runs had been conceded: on this day in India, and then again in the

1999 World Cup semi-final against Australia. In the 154 times that Cronjé bowled in one-day internationals, these two occasions would eventually make it into his best five efforts ever as far as the economy rate is concerned.

The subcontinent also features strongly in the other occasions where Hansie Cronjé's bowling form happened to be at its worst. Point B in Figure 7 (innings 104) refers to South Africa's second match of the Wills Quadrangular tournament in Pakistan at the end of 1997. Point C in Figure 7 (innings 126) refers to a match against West India in South Africa at the beginning of 1999; three of the five matches before that point were however in Bangladesh. Point D in Figure 7 (innings 154) refers to Hansie Cronjé's last match for the Proteas: in the final of the Coca-Cola Cup in Sharjah in March 2000.

*   *   *   *   *

Based on the above, it would appear that a specific analysis of Cronjé's bowling form on the subcontinent might be meaningful. The 8-innings moving average economy rate applicable to Hansie Cronjé's international one-day bowling career is depicted in Figure 8.

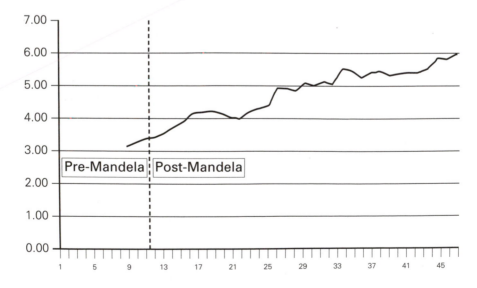

Figure 8 – Hansie Cronjé: 8-innings moving average bowling economy rate (one-day international career – matches on subcontinent only)

Figure 8 does not need any explanation. In this case, the distinction between pre- and post-Mandela is hardly relevant. The fact of the matter is: Hansie Cronjé's bowling form on the subcontinent deteriorated on a continuous basis throughout his career.

*　*　*　*　*

Finally, an analysis should also be done of Hansie Cronjé's 8-innings moving average bowling economy rate in test matches. This is depicted in Figure 9.

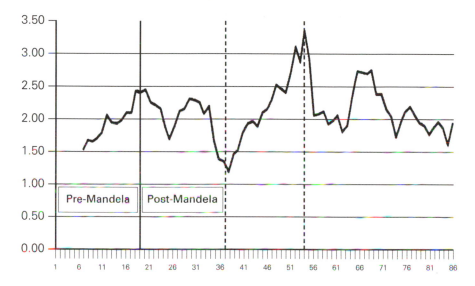

Figure 9 – Hansie Cronjé: 8-innings moving average bowling economy rate (test match career)

Hansie Cronjé's 8-innings moving average bowling economy rate over his test career, as depicted in Figure 9, appears quite volatile and would therefore lead to tenuous conclusions at best.

The only interesting aspect relates to the period where Cronjé appeared to have experienced the most marked deterioration in bowling form, namely from innings 38 up until innings 54 (i.e. between the two dotted lines in Figure 9), as more than half of these occasions were in matches against India and Pakistan.

*   *   *   *   *

The last word belongs to Hansie Cronjé himself. In the interviews on M-Net in August 2000, Mike Haysman asked Cronjé whether he was proud of his career statistics. Cronjé responded as follows:

> It's strange, though, because pre-captain days for South Africa, you're thinking more of stats and you're thinking more of averages and you're thinking more of yourself. The minute I became captain, the team was number one to me; and my goals, my aims were team goals. I wasn't fazed about how many hundreds or averages or bowling or this or that from the time I became captain. It was all about where the team was going, where the team was ranked, what the goals were for the team ...

7

Hansie on Hansie

It had all the elements of a soap opera. An expectant public, glued to their television screens to see if their hero would reveal more than in last night's episode. The hero, involved, by his own admission, in a plot of deceit that even his wife did not know about. The wife herself, blonde and smiling, ever standing by her man. The family intrigue, with model parents getting involved in model son's life gone wrong. The set, complete with designer furniture, expensive leather couches and fancy paintings. And last but not least, the flashback to the previous night's episode: 'The story so far ...'

For three nights in a row, M-Net showed us their interviews with Hansie Cronjé, in peak viewing time. On the Saturday evening it displaced an episode of 'Baywatch', no less – Hansie's wife, Bertha, having to stand in for Pamela Anderson.

The price of the interviews was alleged to be anything between a few hundred thousand rands and a few million rands; nobody would say. A bargain to the television station at any price, it seemed, as the country had to sit through advertisement after advertisement, preceding the programme. In fact, it seemed like a bit of a con: what was promoted as three hours of drama turned out to be only about two-thirds of that, after cutting out all the concomitant promotional material.

After the first night, it certainly appeared as if the advertisers had got their money's worth. According to the official figures of the show, approximately 350,000 M-Net subscribers watched the opening night; an increase of nearly 20% on the number of people watching the pay station during that time slot on an average Thursday evening. This represents a ratio of nearly one in two, in terms of viewers who had access to the programme, given the number of M-Net subscribers in the country. Due to a quirk in the way that the statistics are gathered, the number does not include any of the 450,000 people who may have watched via satellite. If a similar ratio to the 'normal' M-Net subscribers is assumed, this means that well in excess of half a million people tuned in to watch the première of their fallen hero.

The mere fact that Cronjé did the interviews in the first place was viewed by many in rather an unfavourable light. Was it fair that Hansie Cronjé should be paid a substantial amount of money for telling any part of the story about his wrongdoings? Was it fair that he should enrich himself, while people like Herschelle Gibbs and Henry Williams, people whom Cronjé had brought down with him, were banned from playing cricket and cut off from the only source of income they knew?

Probably not. But he did it anyway. And some of us had to watch, I'm afraid. If I wasn't writing a book about it, I don't think I could have sat through more than half of the first interview. And the next two episodes would certainly not have kept me away from Friday night's movie or Saturday night's braai. Totally forgettable, is how I would describe it; 'sanctimonious piffle' was the summary view of a journalist.

An atmosphere of nervous expectation filled the air as Dire Straits' tension-filled *Private Investigations* was played in the opening scene:

> ... treachery and treason – there's always an excuse for it and
> when I find the reason I still can't get used to it ...

A slow guitar, a whispering voice; the music creating a feeling similar to that of a string quartet at a country club, playing for wedding guests sipping sherry as the sun sets.

And the camera angles: sweeping views of Cape Dutch houses and the green, green grass of Fancourt. Outeniqua mountains etched against blue sky in the background ... it would have been a fitting opening to a promotional video for South Africa's tourist authority, or perhaps even the next Olympic bid.

'Hansie, can you believe what's happened to you?' ex-Australian rebel-tourist-turned-television-presenter, Mike Haysman, began. 'It's very, very hard sometimes to sit and you have to pinch yourself to actually realise what the position is at the moment ...' Cronjé replied, in the first of many non-answers, to a set of mostly trivial questions.

To be fair, we couldn't really have expected anything more. With the King Commission set to reconvene some two months later, Cronjé could hardly afford to disclose anything that might be used against him. It was clear that he had been well coached in what should, and should not, be said, and the viewer could not help but feel slightly cheated by such a contrived outcome. A little bit like those wrestlers in the WWF: quite a spectacle, but hardly a spontaneous result. Or, given what's transpired, even a one-day cricket international, some sceptics might add ...

If you needed any proof of the extent to which the questions and answers were scripted, it came in the form of a Mike Haysman interjection. Bertha Cronjé was singing her husband's praises, describing his placid personality and even temper – bubbling away in Afrikaans. Haysman picked his moment and interrupted her, in the most spontaneous fashion, pointing out that he'd heard some dressing-room stories about a very different Mr Cronjé. Now, I'm not sure how much Afrikaans the native from Australia has actually picked up in the time since his decision to settle in South Africa. But I've certainly never seen him react in the same 'natural' manner when people like Fanie de Villiers speak the local language on the cricket show that they would sometimes co-present.

Based on this, it's hardly surprising that the first episode promptly caused a lot of viewers to suffer a relapse of 'Hansie fatigue', and to look for any number of original excuses not to watch the remaining two episodes.

The ratings of the follow-up programmes fully reflect this. A full 40% of the first night's viewers found excuses not to watch any of the next two programmes. Whereas the Thursday night saw the pay station enjoy a gain in market share of some 20%, over the next two evenings M-Net gave back in excess of this to the free-to-air channels, with their bouquet of boring programmes.

When interpreting any interview there are at least two levels of information that need to be considered. The first, and obvious one, is to analyse the discussion itself and to evaluate the answers provided to the questions, as they've been asked. The problem with only focusing on this element, however, is that the vested interests of the person being interviewed inevitably play a part in the way that he or she responds. At the very least, this means that even 'bad news' can be formulated in such a way that it looks somewhat better. In a more extreme scenario, the interviewee can be so economical with the truth that the wrong message can be put across, even though everything that was said may have been technically correct.

In the investment world, for example, an interview with company management (or any presentation they make to the investment community), is one of the elements that typically play a part in the decision of whether to buy, hold or sell a share. The obvious problem, however, is that the people making those presentations are heavily incentivised in terms of ownership arrangements or share incentive schemes. This leads to an inevitable positive bias in what they say and, perhaps more importantly, in what they withhold.

Focusing on the Hansie Cronjé issue itself, there was a very good example of this point found in a statement made by Cronjé and included in an UCBSA press release, dated 8 April 2000 (after the original news had broken, but before Hansie's first confession). Cronjé said, inter alia, the following. '... I want to ensure every South African that I have made a hundred percent effort to win every match that I have played.' What he said meant that he denied ever throwing a match (something that he has stuck to ever since), but what he didn't say in this statement was that he never took money when perhaps he shouldn't have (something which he admitted to soon after).

Another example occurred during testimony before the King Commission by Bronwyn Wilkinson, the Communications Manager of the UCBSA. Wilkinson pointed out how she found it curious that Hansie Cronjé used the singular when he said police could check his bank account at the time of his early denials, as she would have expected him to have more than one account.

One, therefore, has to try and read between the lines. In addition to what was actually said, the question is *how* it was said. Were there any messages in the tone or volume of the voice, the pace of talking or the body language? And what was *not* said? Furthermore, if the interview in question was performed by someone else, the logic can also be extended to ask: what was not asked?

It was interesting to watch Hansie Cronjé's body language during the interviews. For most of it the talented batsman, who once captained South Africa, was totally composed, not batting an eyelid. But there were five occasions where he pulled at his ear, and two more when he touched his nose ... as well as one rub of the cheek and a scratch of the chin.

In his seminal work, *Manwatching: A Field Guide to Human Behaviour*, Desmond Morris discusses a concept which he calls 'nonverbal leakage'. This boils down to a collection of messages that we do not communicate verbally, yet our facial expressions, body movements and gestures provide some clue as to what we really mean when we speak. According to Morris, the number of hand-to-head actions performed by the speaker '... rises dramatically during moments of deception ...'.

The easiest of these movements to understand, are those that attempt to cover the mouth. When false words leave the mouth of the speaker, there is an instinctive reaction to try and cover it up. Most other hand-to-head actions are described as variations of the 'mouth cover', with the hand venturing up towards the face for similar reasons, yet getting deflected at the last moment by the nose, cheek or chin.

The *Collins Gem Body Language* provides a slightly different perspective. According to this work, there are several variants, specifically of rubbing an ear when being interviewed. Whether an ear lobe is pulled, the back of the ear caressed or a fingertip stuck in the ear and rotated, the meaning does, however, remain the same. '... these are all adult equivalents of a child's covering both ears to avoid being scolded for telling a lie.'

Lest undue significance be attached to the various aspects of body language, the Desmond Morris book also warns the reader that a mouth-cover does not necessarily mean a person is lying. It merely points to an increased likelihood of untruthfulness. In Hansie Cronjé's case, one can probably also accept that some of the questions in the Haysman interviews would, by definition, be more difficult to answer than others. With difficulty translating into discomfort, it would be understandable if this, in turn, led to some involuntary movements by the interviewee.

Let's look at the questions and answers from the Hansie interviews that were accompanied with hand-to-head movements made by the previous South African cricket captain.

We didn't have to wait too long for ear pull number one. It occurred as early as question and answer number eight. Mike Haysman asked Hansie Cronjé about the fact that he had kept the story from his immediate family for a number of years. Hansie responded by saying, 'Ja, I mean, if you look back now you've got the sort of advantage of hindsight and it's easy now to say I should have confided in them a long time ago, but it wasn't something that I was proud of ...'

It was a full twenty-four hours later that the audience would witness the first nose touch. Yet it essentially related to the same topic of discussion. This time, Mike Haysman asked Bertha whether she had had any inkling, before Hansie's phone call on the 11th of April, that anything was wrong. Bertha said no at the same time that Hansie's nose required a bit of scratching.

Ear pull number two took place when Haysman asked Hansie why he had denied the first rumours on the 7th of April – obviously an uncomfortable question with which to deal. Cronjé responded as follows. 'I don't know, hey, if I can have it over again, I'll handle it so much differently. I knew that the matches weren't fixed; I knew that the matches were a true reflection of what was going on, the battle between the two sides, and that's what I really denied. I didn't deny that I had conversations with blokes, but I didn't reveal the truth and that is what hurts me as well ...'

From his body language, it would certainly appear that Hansie Cronjé's relationship with the United Cricket Board of South Africa was not an easy line of questioning to undergo. A full three out of the total of nine hand-to-face movements that occurred in the full set of interviews, happened within five minutes during this part of the discussion.

First, there was a rub of the cheek, just as Mike Haysman introduced the topic. Of course, Hansie said all the right things, talking about how good the relationship was, how much he appreciated what they had done for him, and how fantastic Dr Bacher had been throughout his career ...

Then, there was a scratch of the chin. The conversation had turned to the political pressures on the team, and the prescribed 'quotas' of black players that were suggested shortly before the 1999 World Cup. Cronjé's furious reaction at the time, and how he stormed out of the meeting, for example, was public knowledge.

Soon after, we saw ear pull number three, when Hansie, flashing a rare smile, told Haysman about leaving Johannesburg and disappearing to Bloemfontein for a day.

In addition to all the mouth-cover variants as discussed, it was also worth noting how different other aspects of Hansie Cronjé's body language were during this part of the discussion, compared to the remainder of the interviews. It was made obvious that his opinions about affirmative action in the sport were very strong. This was certainly evident from what he said, but even more so from the way that he said it: forceful hand movements, a louder voice, a faster pace, a different pitch. In fact, this reminded one of the 'old' Hansie Cronjé; the skilled orator, not the nervous individual who had to count all his words over a number of months.

There was one interesting observation made by Hansie Cronjé during this part of the conversation, when he said, 'I grew up in a totally different time and era in South Africa, call it post-apartheid, where everybody was equal and everybody had equal opportunity, and I didn't see any reason why people should be judged differently.'

Although this may have been largely true in the 90s, the period during which Cronjé played international cricket, it certainly did not apply to the time when he was growing up in the 70s and 80s. In fact, many people will argue that there's still a big difference between political equality in terms of voting rights and the abolition of discriminatory legislation in South Africa, on the one hand, and equal opportunity, on the other. Equal opportunity, in its wider sense, will take at least one or two generations to come to fruition. It will only be applicable once a more normalised distribution of wealth has been achieved in the country, for example, which will translate into equal access to schooling and other facilities.

Returning to Hansie Cronjé and his opinions, it is important to bear in mind, at this point, that there is a lot of evidence demonstrating that Hansie was not against the various aspects of development cricket. He merely had his own opinions about the way in which one should go about it.

A final point needs to be made about the relationship between Hansie Cronjé and the UCBSA and, more specifically, the fact that this appeared to be a difficult part of the M-Net interviews for Cronjé to handle, from a body language perspective. When probed on this very point before the King Commission, Cronjé was reluctant to give any sort of answer. In response to a question by Shamila Batohi, Cronjé said, 'I think it will be very dangerous for me at this stage, Mr Commissioner. I don't want to get into a situation where I disclose my relationship with the United Cricket Board ...' In the event, Judge King conceded to the 'objection' by the witness, and requested that Batohi proceed to her next question. The topic was not mentioned again until the Commission adjourned.

Ear pull number four was executed when Mike Haysman questioned Hansie Cronjé about an incident which occurred during the 1997-1998 tour of Australia. At the time, there was video evidence where Cronjé himself was involved in treading on the ball. There were no real consequences at the time, but it's obviously something that Hansie still doesn't particularly enjoy talking about.

Ear pull number five soon followed. It was only a couple of questions later that Haysman asked Hansie about the 1999 World Cup. Once again, this is not the most pleasant memory for Cronjé to recall. His performance, both as a player and as a captain, over the course of a tournament in which South Africa stumbled when they were expected to win, has been criticised and questioned by many. It is also discussed elsewhere in this book.

Which leaves nose touch number two. This was reserved for a question about a book relating to the whole affair, with which Hansie Cronjé was supposedly busy. Cronjé denied that there had been any progress with such a book, and said that the final few chapters of his life first needed to transpire before a book could be contemplated whatsoever. He was at pains to point out that the intention of the book would be for other people to benefit from his mistakes. It will certainly be interesting to see how soon after the final findings of the King Commission, the Hansie Cronjé book is actually released.

What else could be said about the Hansie & Haysie show? Firstly, a point or two about the interviewers themselves. It was interesting that Mike Haysman was chosen to pose most of the questions, given the fact that he was the television presenter who received a rather prominent mention at the time of the King Commission. During cross-examination, Hansie Cronjé, himself, told Shamila Batohi that, according to Marlon Aronstam, Haysman had mentioned to him that '... the result at Centurion Park had nothing to do with cricket, but had more to do with the fact that Mr Aronstam had money on the game ...'. Yet this point never came up between Hansie and Haysman during the M-Net interviews ...

Furthermore, Haysman did not do himself any favours in the way that he went about questioning Cronjé. There was hardly an incisive question, and most of the interview had a ring of hero worship to it. In fact, the viewer could be forgiven for wondering who was actually paying whom for these programmes!

The bowling equivalent of the typical question that was posed, would either be a slow full-toss, or a long hop outside off-stump. Contenders for worst question of the programme included:

- 'How would you rate your childhood, and your first years playing for South Africa?' (How do these two points even relate to each other?)
- 'Putting it on a bit of a scale, how wrong do you think you've actually done? I mean, we all know worldwide there's murderers still walking around, that sort of stuff, how wrong do you think you've done?' (Was he actually serious, asking this?)
- 'Obviously one of your greatest pressures right now, is making sure you qualify for the indemnity from criminal prosecution. Have you spoken the truth?' (As if Hansie would use this forum to admit if he hadn't?)
- 'Hansie, over the years, I'm sure you've collected some seriously nice cricket memorabilia. What is something that is very special to you?' (Does anybody care?)

And then there was Marianne Kriel. A bronze medallist at the 1996 Olympics in the 100 metres backstroke, this was her debut as a television presenter. Most people would probably agree that the job of asking difficult questions didn't come naturally to her either. After all, swimming has never been known as a sport during which people communicate much.

Kriel's low point came in the form of the following question. 'Hansie, it just seems to someone like me, who isn't as involved in cricket, that someone like Shane Warne, who did similar things, got away a lot easier, and that the same crime wasn't punished as big as it was in South Africa. What do you think of that?'

Firstly, the 'someone who isn't as involved in cricket' part certainly got the prize for understatement of the evening. Secondly, it was an opinion, not a question. And thirdly, from what we know about the Shane Warne affair, it could certainly not be equated to asking your colleagues to play badly.

As with every other question, Cronjé would not even take the bait when the opportunity to knock the Aussies was on offer. But Mike Haysman couldn't wait to offer his opinion, however, agreeing with Kriel's misconstruction, and calling the manner in which the Australian situation had been handled, 'disgraceful'.

There were other weak questions. 'Bertha, it seemed to me like you and Hansie enjoy laughing together' springs to mind. And, 'One day, when you do have children, it's obviously going to be important for you to share this with them; this whole experience. How are you going to approach them?' was another. Many questions were repeated, some up to three times in various forms. As mentioned before, they were three *long* programmes to sit through ...

In addition to the more 'difficult' questions, nothing of real significance came out of the interviews. Hansie Cronjé said, on a number of occasions, that he'd made a mistake, how sorry he was about it, and that he realised there would be consequences. He reiterated that matches had never been thrown. He spoke about his psychiatric treatment, the antidepressants that he was using and the death threats that he'd received. He pointed no fingers, and only had glowingly positive things to say about everybody else, even when probed about people like Bob Woolmer and Ali Bacher, where the differences between him and some of these people were well documented. He spoke about his upbringing, and stressed how much family and friends had meant to him during the crisis. He spoke about his religion; about the fact that being a Christian did not mean that one didn't make mistakes, and how forgiving oneself was the most difficult aspect. He denied that he had too much control over the team. He hinted at some of his future business plans, mentioning the internet, financial services and pharmaceuticals as areas of interest.

Discussing 'the mistake' that he'd made, Hansie Cronjé continuously focused on the passing on of a 'snippet of information' – as if that was the only thing that he'd ever done wrong. Even when discussing the approach that Hansie had made to Herschelle Gibbs and Henry Williams later on in the programme, Haysman followed this up by asking whether that was the only time that Cronjé had spoken to anyone to 'try and undermine their performance'. Responding in the affirmative, Cronjé seemed to conveniently forget about the approaches to Pieter Strydom, Jacques Kallis, Mark Boucher and Lance Klusener, during the same tour to India. Or the earlier approaches to Pat Symcox in 1995, or the whole team in 1996. But Haysman didn't point this out, or question Cronjé about it either.

Perhaps the most fascinating point of all three interviews was when Hansie Cronjé said the toughest part for him during the King Commission, was 'when Herschelle said that he obviously looked up to his captain, and he felt that if his captain could do it, then so could he'. Why was this so interesting? Well, speaking for myself, I don't think I'm ever likely to make a mistake about the *toughest part* of any bad experience, whether it's a wipeout in a motorcar accident, a washout on the golf course or a whiteout on the ski slopes.

But in Hansie's case, his memory didn't serve him well when reflecting on the toughest part of the King Commission. He actually referred to Herschelle's words ('… if his captain could do it, then so could he …') on two separate occasions. Yet Herschelle never uttered these words himself … Henry Williams did, twice.

Hansie Cronjé was also asked about the state of his relationship with Allan Donald. Pointing out that they had been friends since the age of seven or eight, Cronjé admitted that Donald had told him about his disappointment relating to what Cronjé had done. Donald was also quite critical of Hansie's actions in the press, where it was reported that Donald had said he would probably not speak to Cronjé again, and that Cronjé 'had better start running' if the allegations levelled against him were true. It was also reported that Donald had phoned Cronjé and spoken to his parents while Hansie was in the house, yet Cronjé did not return the call. Donald even received a mention at the King Commission when Shamila Batohi quoted from his autobiography, wherein he called Cronjé's decision to declare at Centurion 'just ridiculous'.

But Hansie said, during the interviews, that the relationship with Allan was back on track, and they had spoken on two occasions since the scandal had broken. Call me a cynic, but two occasions do not amount to many over a period of three to four months, especially when the two people concerned are long-term friends and one of them is, by all accounts, more desperate for support than he might ever again be in his life.

When asked his opinion about the investigation into the affairs of players in India, and specifically the $50 million that Mohammed

Azharuddin had allegedly 'earned' through wrongdoing, Hansie Cronjé stressed that this issue related only to income tax, and not to bribery or match-fixing. Cronjé did, however, neglect to address the issue of how Azharuddin ever got his hands on such a substantial amount of money in the first place (assuming that he did). And neither did Haysman push him on this. But then, of course, we know that Cronjé and Azharuddin were friends …

There was more evidence of Cronjé's attitude towards money, when he was asked why he chose cricket over rugby, another sport in which he had shown tremendous potential. The reason? Because '… cricket was going to pay for your studies rather than rugby'. But rugby scholarships at the University of the Orange Free State would have been at least as attractive as those for cricket, at the time. The real reason can safely be assumed, therefore, to relate to the fact that a long-term career in cricket would have appeared far more profitable at that stage, during the days of rugby 'shamateurism'.

What was particularly curious, was when Hansie Cronjé spoke about his ideas on welfare and community service. 'The more you give, the more you receive, and that's a principle that you often forget about,' were his very words.

Exemplary? Or just very ironic? Take your pick. Just bear in mind that Cronjé once offered $15,000 to Herschelle Gibbs to throw his wicket, but that he was going to take a turn of $10,000 for himself in the process. But Haysman forgot to ask him about this.

Hansie's wife Bertha put on a brave face and responded smilingly to all the questions put to her, while firmly clasping her husband's hand. Judging from her answers, Hansie's involvement with bookmakers must be the best thing that could ever have happened to the couple. Now, at last, they could spend some time together. And everybody had just been so *wonderful* …

It seemed as if every second word uttered by Bertha was 'wonderful'. The first night she used the word on no less than sixteen occasions. I gave up counting on the second night.

Bertha told us about the two suitcases full of letters and e-mails of support that they'd received. She told us about the strength of their marriage and their religion. And, of course, she told us how absolutely wonderful her friends, her parents and everybody else had been.

We were also told about the weekend they spent together between first news of the betting scandal and Hansie's first confession. They neglected to remind us, however, that Saturday the 8th of April 2000, when Hansie was still withholding the truth from Bertha, was also the date of their fifth wedding anniversary. One to forget, no doubt.

Hansie and Bertha spoke about their loyalty to South Africa, as well as the fact that they would never contemplate leaving the country. Whether any of this related to the danger that Cronjé might be arrested outside of South Africa (and extradited to India) was, however, not addressed.

Hansie's parents, Ewie and San-Marie Cronjé, also made an appearance. Ewie, in his day also a cricketer of note, captained Free State in the 60s and scored an unbeaten 70 runs against the Australian touring side of 1966-1967. He was seen at the King Commission every day, supporting his son.

The two of them put up a brave showing. Perhaps the most significant moment was when both of them spoke about the mood swings that they had noticed in Hansie. According to Ewie, every time his son took money he was at a low.

The other comment of Ewie's that stood out, was when he said he wondered if there would have been investigations if Hansie had not come out with the truth on the 11th of April. This seemed to presuppose that Hansie would have made a confession even if there had not been any phone transcripts or other evidence. And one should not forget that he volunteered only a fraction of the truth that day.

*   *   *   *   *

There have, of course, been other opportunities for us to learn about the Hansie Cronjé persona and personality, from the man himself. One of these was his testimony before the King Commission, when a nation watched their fallen idol face bouncers, googlies and flippers, delivered by some of the best legal brains in the country.

In particular, Cronjé was forthcoming about his love of money. By his own admission, he had more than enough of it, yet he couldn't resist the temptation to acquire more, in dubious ways. One of his answers that will always stand out, was when he said:

175

> I at no stage had any worries about cost of living. In fact, I think
> I actually saved most of my meal allowances and sustenance
> allowances because of the generosity of South African restau-
> rant owners and friends, and my team-mates will also tell you
> that I wasn't always the first one to take the wallet out when we
> were buying a round of drinks.

Hansie Cronjé also provided details of his assets and investments. He was clearly informed about the financial markets, referring to the NASDAQ, the Dow Jones and the FTSE, as well as various trust accounts and investment arrangements with Merrill Lynch. In one of his responses, Cronjé said, 'I think one of the advantages of being a cricketer is that you have your ear close to the market, not only in this country, but also worldwide and we have access to some of the best newspapers and business reports ...'

The previous point is worth noting, as Cronjé later testified that Marlon Aronstam had revealed to him '... that he was involved with NSI, a listed company, which I now know to be involved in sports betting. I did not know this at the time and only became aware of it in April of this year.' I may be wrong, but when somebody tells you that he is involved with a listed company, it would seem natural to enquire about the company's line of business – especially when you're as financially astute as the previous captain of the South African cricket team evidently was.

Hansie Cronjé obviously had a tough few days at the King Commission. One can, perhaps, not blame him for the fact that he appeared to come across somewhat aggressively towards the end of it. At one point, he said the following to Judge King. '... I don't ask you personal questions as to what you talk about over lunch time, and I think it's very harsh to ask me to reveal that. I can promise you from my side that it's not anything to do with money or bribery or related matters, whether it goes back to the 1900s or the 1800s, Mr. Commissioner.'

This was followed by a slight role reversal a short while later: Hansie Cronjé began to ask some questions himself. He wanted to know whether he was being tried on the information that had been in the media.

Shortly thereafter, Cronjé arguably came across more strongly than at any other point in his three days of cross-examination. Beginning with,

'Excuse me, Mr. Commissioner, can I speak?' he proceeded to talk for almost two minutes, describing how he believed that the line of questioning being followed, was unfair. When Judge King attempted to interrupt him midway through the address, Cronjé responded by saying, 'I just want to finish, Mr Commissioner'. And finish he did.

Hansie Cronjé, the joker, was also seen at the King Commission. But that's a topic for another chapter.

8

The lighter side

The public image that Hansie Cronjé created around himself, over the years, has certainly not been that of a joker. In fact, some people might argue that he was quite dour. Remember Bob Woolmer's reference to the 'epitome of the unsmiling Afrikaaner'? Always serious, driven and fiercely competitive …

Some of this may be ascribed to the 'Kepler effect', as the previous captain of the South African cricket team never aspired to having a nice-guy image, either. As a top sportsman, you don't particularly want to be the nice guy, as 'nice guys come second'. There are many examples of this: Pete Sampras and Tiger Woods spring to mind, when one thinks about world-class achievers who hardly ever smile, until they serve the last ace or sink the last putt.

Never was Hansie Cronjé's emotional control brought to the fore more than the day that he read his comprehensive statement to the King Commission, on 15 June 2000. Unflinching, he kept the straightest of faces and hardly ever looked up. For more than half an hour, he maintained the same tone of voice. Of course, there weren't any smiles that day. There was, after all, very little to smile about.

Before that, Hansie certainly did have his moments. The smile that was generally reserved for the trophy ceremony (of which, to be fair, there were many) was sometimes flashed when he took a good catch, or an important breakthrough was made by another member of the team. Many will agree that Cronjé's brilliant smile was a most disarming one, as is the case when most serious people do smile (especially those in

179

important positions). In Hansie's case, the quality of his features would further add to the impact: the deep eyes, the perfect set of teeth – enough to make any mother's heart melt.

Hansie capitalised on the scarcity value of his smile, in a number of television advertisements that had a humorous slant. In one for a well-known chain of steak-houses, Cronjé and Paul Adams set quite a bad example for children, essentially playing with their food while exchanging lots of laughter and light banter. But the Hansie advert that will probably be best remembered, was for a bank that sponsored night cricket in South Africa. In this, he hits a big six that knocks out one of the stadium spotlights. In the resulting power failure, the whole city is left in the dark. A mischievous-looking Hansie shrugs his shoulders and simply says, 'Sorry'. We will probably never see this advertisement again, but the memory will linger on … reinforced by the number of times that Hansie ended up saying sorry to family, team-members and fans alike, after the scandal broke.

Hansie Cronjé could also crack a few jokes of his own. The day that he fed Paddy Upton (the team's fitness trainer at the time) two sleeping pills, will probably go down as one of his most famous practical jokes, ever. Upton was told they were malaria tablets. He eventually passed out on the grass, whilst on-duty, during a World Cup match.

Kepler Wessels provides a vivid description of the Hansie Cronjé sense of humour, in his biography. He relays an account of the day that Hansie won the Man of the Match award, in a one-day international against the West Indies, at Newlands, in February 1993. Cronjé scored a quick 31 runs and followed this up with bowling figures of 3/27 on the day. President F.W. de Klerk was at the presentation ceremony, and when Hansie got his award, the 23-year old cricketer wrapped his one arm around the President. Hansie was about to start pouring champagne all over Mr de Klerk with the other, but Kepler quickly intervened. 'No, Hansie. Stop. You can't do that. It's the Prez. Stop it.'

At a benefit golf day of his, which was held at Fancourt, in March 1998, Cronjé was the main speaker at the ensuing prize-giving. I will never forget how pleasantly surprised a friend of mine was with Hansie's sense of humour, when relaying an account of the events to me afterwards. I still recall a number of the jokes that Cronjé had told, and the one that will probably go down best in print, was when he commented on the new phenomenon at big sports events, where members of the crowd would get involved more than ever before. For example, he said, when Mark Fish (prominent defender of the South African soccer team) got the ball, a number of people would pull out cans of pickled fish, and everyone would shout 'Feeeeesh!' And when his team-mate, the midfielder, John Moshoeu (popularly referred to as 'Shoes'), got the ball, many people would pull off their shoes and everyone would shout 'Shooeeeees!' Hansie was worried, he said, that the trend might spill over to rugby – and just imagine what the crowd might get up to if ever Dick Muir got the ball!

As is the case with most disasters, there were a lot of jokes doing the rounds, within hours of people realising that Hansie was, in fact, guilty of something more than a temporary loss of form. 'Hansie Cronjé – the best captain money can buy', would become one of the most popular one-liners. Every red-blooded South African with an e-mail address, started receiving messages ranging from a mock new national anthem to brain teasers, such as: What does a castaway do when his only match breaks whilst trying to light a candle? Phone Hansie, of course – he fixes matches!

David Kau, a black stand-up comedian, whose usual repertoire would not typically include jokes about a topic which is essentially confined to white South Africa, devoted about 20% of a show of his, in June 2000, to the Hansie saga. In his bemused observation, he hadn't seen white people 'being pissed off *en masse* like this, since the day Nelson Mandela was released from prison!'. As one of those white people, I can only admit that Kau touched a nerve; not about being 'pissed off', but certainly about the magnitude of the various forms of emotional turbulence that many people went through, on both of the occasions to which he refers. And let me hasten to add, that there were indeed few, if any, similarly talked-about examples, in the intervening ten-year period.

Well-known South African cartoonist, Zapiro, also went to town on the Hansie Cronjé affair, producing approximately ten different satirical pictures over the time that the story unfolded. The sequence of cartoons portrayed many aspects, including Hansie Cronjé's contribution to an evolving scenario of unethical behaviour, in South African public life, the question as to how much of the truth was actually out, the impact of a fallen role model on hero-worshipping children, and the damage done to the image and popularity of South African cricket.

And so to the King Commission. Throughout proceedings, Judge Edwin King exhibited a keen sense of humour, not only in some of his remarks and questions, but also by smiling warmly, quite often. And some of the other people who testified raised some real chuckles …

There were, for example, a number of humorous moments towards the end of Henry Williams's testimony. In response to a question about his background, asked by Jeremy Gauntlett (acting for the UCBSA), Williams mentioned his involvement with a company called SFW. 'You wouldn't know this, Mr Gauntlett, but SFW is a winery,' the judge said, to general laughter. In typically stilted legal-speak, Gauntlett retorted, 'I am appreciative, Mr Commissioner, that in certain and many respects, your knowledge exceeds that of anyone in the room.'

This interplay seemed even funnier a few weeks later, when Judge King told a reporter, in an interview, how he'd become an instantly recognisable personality due to the publicity surrounding the commission's work. He went on to relate how embarrassed he had felt, on one occasion, when he was seen buying only a few bottles of wine at a supermarket. According to the article, the judge actually felt compelled to tell the people around him that his wife was the one responsible for buying the food!

Then, in response to a question by Shamila Batohi as to whether

Williams thought the conditions in Nagpur favoured his bowling to such an extent that the decision for the seamer to open the bowling could be justified, Williams discussed the other bowlers and referred to one 'Elvis' Elworthy. To which the Commissioner promptly replied, '... Elvis is probably related to Banjo'.

As discussed earlier, there's also little doubt about Hansie Cronje's well-developed sense of humour. The extent to which this very point featured in evidence before the King Commission, has already been discussed elsewhere in this book. In short, a number of people seemed to believe that it played a large part in Cronjé's downfall. A weak joke, gone horribly wrong.

Although his first appearance before the King Commission was rather stony-faced, there was lots of evidence of Hansie Cronjé's lighter side in the two and a half days of cross-examination that followed. On a number of occasions Hansie would make light of serious moments in order, perhaps, to deflect the tension inherent in the proceedings.

One of the comic highlights of the hearings occurred when the serious matter of the team meeting, regarding the 1996 Mumbai offer, was the topic of cross-examination. Shamila Batohi wanted to

The lighter side

183

know from Hansie Cronjé which specific players were for, and against, the proposal.

Cronjé was clearly in high spirits at that point; he would even use Judge King's affectionate nickname in his answer. 'Ma'am, if you go into a selection meeting, and there are five selectors, we all discuss. And some players play devil's advocate, some selectors will play devil's advocate, so it is very dangerous to walk out of a selection meeting and say that Mike Procter definitely wanted Sharky King to play in the next game, and that was just because he was being devil's advocate to try and push for … to put the other side as well.'

And 'Sharky' was quick to respond. 'Is that the same devil that has previously been mentioned in these proceedings, Mr Cronjé?' he asked, to tumultuous laughter. The reference was to Hansie Cronjé's inclusion of the role of Satan, in his original confession, on 11 April 2000.

What nobody pointed out, however, was that Hansie Cronjé's original point might have been humorous, but it was certainly far from appropriate. When it's decided which members of a squad will be selected to fill a limited number of positions in a line-up there obviously needs to be an open discussion about the potential value added by each individual (as pointed out by Cronjé). But in matters of ethical behaviour,

'… and nothing but the truth'?

184

there's only one set of guidelines that should ever apply – no real room for any devil's advocate.

At times, more humour was introduced into the King Commission than could actually be justified by the gravity of the case. This would, once or twice, result in a situation where someone would obviously try to be funny, and everyone else would probably have caught the joke, as we're not talking about the subtlest of humour here. Yet few people laughed. The timing was wrong; the mood had to be serious.

One of the best examples of this, was when there seemed to be a measure of confusion regarding the exact identity of one Sanjay Chawla, the Indian bookmaker, who featured prominently in Hansie Cronjé's testimony. He was also known as Sanjeev, and there was further uncertainty as to whether his surname was actually spelt Chawla or Chowla.

The Commissioner asked, 'Will the real Mr. Sanjay please stand up?' There was some laughter, but Mr Cronjé clearly didn't find it funny from the witness box.

There wouldn't be any jokes for some time after that. Something special was to follow, however.

Never during the course of the King Commission's proceedings, was there an occasion that unified the Commissioner, the witness *cum* prime suspect, the chief investigator and the audience more, than when Shamila Batohi expressed her concern over the difficulty of her next line of questioning (relating to the alleged transcripts of the telephone conversations).

She found encouragement and support from an unlikely source: Hansie Cronjé, himself. 'We had an obligation at the start, that we're both on the same side, so we're going to try our best,' Cronjé said, referring to a shared commitment to unveiling the truth. 'I'm encouraged to hear that,' Batohi responded. And then, Judge Edwin King produced the funniest and most heart-warming moment of the hearings. 'The two of you on the same side; I'm not taking any bets,' he said. This time, everybody laughed.

Earlier, Hansie Cronjé had also made a light-hearted reference to betting. He was talking about the difficult circumstances that the team was finding itself in, at the time that they were discussing the 1996 offer in Mumbai. Cronjé ended off by saying, '... so if I was a betting man, and I would think that a lot of the people in the room will believe that by now, I would probably have put money on India, yes.' Funny? Or was there a more serious suggestion here?

Hansie Cronjé did, of course, go through all of the challenging hearings of the King Commission in his second language. Yet he seemed to cope perfectly, until a question by Brendan Manca, acting for the UCBSA, referred to his 'fastidious habits'.

'Sorry, what's fastidious?' Cronjé wanted to know. Manca started explaining that he was referring to Cronjé's careful approach to working with money, but soon realised that it was perhaps not the right word in the first place. He changed his mind to 'parsimonious'.

'Stingy,' the Commissioner suggested.

People laughed. More importantly, they also understood.

Just before the sad conclusion to Hansie Cronjé's testimony, there were a few, final chuckles. When Shamila Batohi asked Cronjé whether his wife might discover some more dollars lying around in their house, he said, 'I think if my wife discovers one more dollar lying in the house, she'll cut the other testicle out as well ...'

Immediately thereafter, Batohi asked Hansie Cronjé what he planned

to do with the illegitimate money that he'd obtained. Cronjé was evasive, saying that he did not want it to appear as if he was 'trying to put a positive thought in the Commissioner's mind'.

'Don't forget impoverished Commissioners, when you make up your mind, Mr Cronjé …' Judge Edwin King said, moments later. After that, Hansie Cronjé broke down in tears.

9

Final thoughts

In this book, the Hansie Cronjé saga has been looked at from different angles. Various people who know Hansie were consulted in the process. The statistics of Cronjé's form, over time, have been looked into. And various elements of the King Commission have been analysed.

But what other lessons are there to heed? With some hindsight, the answer seems simple. There have been many lessons over time, staring us in the face, if only we cared to take notice. Let's take a look at some of them.

Lessons from India

There would appear to be an Indian connection in most of the transgressions to which Hansie Cronjé has admitted.

The Mandela Trophy approach in 1995 was made by 'an Indian or Pakistani man'. Then, somebody named Sunil approached Cronjé on the 1996 tour to India. Shortly thereafter, Cronjé's association with one MK Gupta began. (This included the Mumbai offer, discussed by the team.) Gupta was introduced to Cronjé by former Indian captain, Mohammed Azharuddin.

Move forward by three years, to the start of Cronjé's association with Sanjay Chawla. On the subsequent tour to India, Cronjé made three documented approaches to team-mates, asking them to underperform. In fact, the only known transgression of which Cronjé was ever guilty,

189

without any Indian connection, was when he provided information to Marlon Aronstam.

The part played by a variety of Indian people in the Hansie Cronjé saga is somewhat ironic, as it is a well-known fact that cricket links between South Africa and India have been very strong over the years. There are many reasons for this.

Go back in history, just more than a decade, to the 80s. South Africa was going through a most pronounced phase of political turmoil. The African National Congress (ANC) was banned in its own country; this despite the fact that it would be the ruling party with close on a two-thirds majority only a few years later. And while the ANC could not have an office in South Africa (an official one anyway), they had one of their overseas offices in India at the time. To this is attached a great deal of history.

There is a large Indian community in South Africa, none of whom would ever personify their resistance to the unjust laws of the country more famously than Mahatma Gandhi in the early part of the twentieth century. Years later, a large number of people of Indian descent would feature strongly in the top structures of the ANC, as well as the new South African government since 1994.

With cricket being the premier sport in India, it is no coincidence that South Africans of Indian descent have also avidly played and followed the game over the years. Although there are no players of Indian origin in the Protea squad today, the reason for this can no doubt be ascribed to a lack of opportunity, against the political background of the country during the latter part of the twentieth century.

This was, of course, not always the case. In the late 60s a Combined Non-White XI, the majority of whom were of Indian descent, beat a Johnny Waite XI, which included most of the all-white test squad who would go on to trounce the Australian touring side shortly thereafter. Yet the 'Indian' players could not be considered to represent the country of their birth at the time. Understandably, this led to much bitterness, and many of the older-generation South African cricket lovers of Indian descent still find it difficult to support the Proteas.

Based on the political links between South Africa and India, as described above, it was no surprise when Mr Jagmohan Dalmiya, who was Indian Board secretary at the time and went on to become President of the ICC, facilitated South Africa's return to international cricket in 1991 (a year after Nelson Mandela's release from prison). And it was even less of a surprise when South Africa reciprocated immediately by sending its first post-isolation touring squad to India, to play in three one-day international matches in November 1991.

But, unfortunately, matters were destined to go full circle. Less than ten years later the biggest scandal ever to hit South African cricket would break in India, when the phone transcripts implicating Hansie Cronjé were released by Delhi police.

Despite betting on cricket being illegal in India, it is widely known that it is a very big 'industry' in that country. Nearly anything that can happen in a game is subject to a bet, from the win of the toss to the Man of the Match. Not to mention the number of runs that a batsman will score, or the colour of face paint that a player will wear. And the market is active. It moves with every ball that is bowled, as the game develops.

According to reports, the total amount wagered on any given one-day match involving India, exceeds $200 million. Given that the major international teams play upwards of thirty such matches per annum, this translates into a total annual betting market of more than $6 billion.

Rumours of match-fixing have been coming out of India for years. In one of the most high-profile incidents, top all-rounder Manoj Prabhakar made revelations after his retirement from the game in 1997. Although he didn't mention any names at the time, Prabhakar spoke about an offer he had received from a senior team-mate, to play badly in a match against Pakistan in 1994.

Not long thereafter, former Pakistani wicketkeeper, Rashid Latif, was quoted in the press implicating four Indian players (including Mohammed Azharuddin). He later denied that he had made the allegations.

Although Prabhakar's allegations, specifically, were not taken seriously by many, the pressure mounted on the Indian Board to begin doing something about this issue. Whilst Board secretary, Jagmohan Dalmiya, affirmed his belief in the players' innocence, former Chief Justice, Y.V. Chandrachud, began a one-man probe. But his investigation found nothing and was, subsequently, not made public. Prabhakar was considered the villain for crying wolf.

Dalmiya went on to become President of the ICC soon after, and would preside over matters during one of the most turbulent two-year periods in the game's history. In the early part of his reign the Mark Waugh/Shane Warne information scandal broke, and just before he was replaced as president, it was Hansiegate. Towards the end of his reign Dalmiya, himself, was subject to allegations of irregularities relating to the award of television rights by the ICC.

Dr Ali Bacher had the following to say about Dalmiya in his evidence before the King Commission: 'I know him for more than a decade. He, in fact, was the driving force in 1991 to get South Africa back into international cricket. So we have a long, long association. He's under siege at the moment, which is sad. There are question marks about his integrity, and I made it very clear to him yesterday, on the phone, that he has my support. I would not question his integrity …'

The words had an eerie ring to them. On the 7th April 2000, the UCBSA released a press statement shortly after the first news of the Hansie Cronjé scandal had broken. The statement referred to the fact that Dr Bacher had spoken to the South African captain and concluded, 'Cronjé is known for his unquestionable integrity and honesty.'

A few weeks after the first round of hearings of the King Commission had been concluded, 300 income tax officials were involved in 'Operation Gentleman', raiding the houses of prominent Indian players and officials – including Dalmiya. Notable exclusions from the raids were batting prodigy Sachin Tendulkar, opener Rahul Dravid and captain Saurav Ganguly.

Meanwhile, the Central Bureau of Investigation (CBI) in India was making progress with a probe into corruption in the country's cricket. Players who had been implicated and were under investigation, included Mohammed Azharuddin, Ajay Jadeja and Nikhil Chopra. When the Indian squad for the ICC knockout trophy in Kenya was announced at the beginning of September 2000, all three of these players were omitted.

Ten days later, Indian coach, and one of the biggest names in Indian cricket, Kapil Dev, resigned from his position. Dev had also become subject to the CBI probe, specifically after being named, in May, as the cricketer who had approached Prabhakar in 1994.

The CBI report was scheduled to be submitted to Indian Sports Minister SS Dhindsa before the end of September 2000. A few days before the due date it was announced, however, that it would be delayed to the beginning of October. The cricket world waits with bated breath.

One of the hottest topics of speculation is the extent to which administrators may feature in the CBI's findings, especially given the strong views of IS Bindra, former President of the Board of Control for Cricket in India (BCCI). Bindra has been quoted as saying that '... the role of administrators are 95% ... if you shut your eyes and ears or join in, then it's very easy'.

One more incident from India deserves to be mentioned. At the time of the 1999 World Cup, Indian journalist Pradeep Magazine published a book called *Not Quite Cricket*, subtitled *The Explosive Story of How Bookmakers Influence the Game Today*. In the early part of the book the author essentially tells his own story of how he was approached by people from the betting world to get introductions to some of India's most high-profile players. In return, Magazine was promised a house in Delhi, in a locality of his choice. Initially, he played along ... but only to get a story. When he eventually disclosed his experience in the press, in 1997, few people believed him, and he was condemned for bringing Indian cricket into disrepute.

Pradeep Magazine makes a few other interesting observations in his book. He explains the role of those who gather information, and how it is their love of the game that is said to take them on their cricket travels around the world. He mentions how much more frequent the telephonic contact becomes at the time of a match. Once, a bookmaker bought him a cellphone. Compare this to Hansie's gift of a cellphone during the tour to India in 2000.

He explains how important it is to have the captain on your side. And on two occasions, he mentions how South Africa featured prominently in the activities of the bookmakers with whom he dealt.

What are the lessons from India? The Manoj Prabhakar allegations (and those from Rashid Latif), as well as the original Pradeep Magazine article, all saw the light at around the same time, in 1997. Yet an initial judicial probe appeared to sweep them under the carpet and it took authorities a full two years to react.

But, as is so often the case, it would appear that the age-old maxim held true once more: where there's smoke, there's almost certainly fire.

The lessons, therefore, come in the form of questions. How could the 1996 offer, to the South African team in Mumbai and a well-known

Final thoughts

193

incident to many, have been swept under the carpet for so long? Why did nobody properly follow up some of the allegations made in Pradeep Magazine's book, insofar as they insinuate some kind of South African involvement? And, most of all, how could South Africans have been so arrogant as to believe that their players would always be beyond reproach in a cricket world littered with incidents and rumours, given that what is ultimately dealt with here is the love of money, one of mankind's oldest vices?

Lessons from Australia

Cricketers from Down Under have certainly played their part, as the history of betting in the sport unfolded over the last two decades.

No discussion of betting in cricket can be complete without referring to, perhaps, the most famous incident ever. In July 1981, during the Ashes series in England, Australia was well in control in the third test at Headingley. They had scored 401 in the first innings and England could only manage to score 174 in reply. Following on, England was soon 135 for 7 in their second innings. The experts agreed: there was simply no chance that they could win the match from that position; draw maybe, but never win. Yet Australian players Rod Marsh and Dennis Lillee heard that there were odds of 500 to 1 available for England to win anyway. They decided to have a flutter and laid down a £10 bet. Then Ian Botham played one of his best, and probably his most important, innings ever for England. Having gone in at number 7, he scored an unbeaten 149. England amassed a total of 356 and Australia was promptly bowled out for 111 on the last day. England won by 18 runs – only the second time ever that a side, following on in a test, went on to win. Marsh and Lillee collected their winnings, but got into trouble for it – notwithstanding the fact that Dennis Lillee, at number ten, obtained Australia's third-highest score.

In 1995, Mark Waugh, Shane Warne and Tim May accused Salim Malik of making an offer to them to throw a match five months before. It led to a series of denials, counteraccusations and bad press. Five years later, Malik would eventually receive a life ban from the sport.

In December 1998 it was announced that the Australian Cricket Board had secretly fined Mark Waugh and Shane Warne at the beginning of 1995, for providing information to bookmakers. It led to an uproar: these were, after all, the same players who had accused Salim Malik of wrongdoing. And why the secrecy?

A week later, the Australian Cricket Board (ACB) launched a Player Conduct Inquiry under Rob O'Regan, AM QC. O'Regan's brief was to look into all matters from 1992 onwards. A total of 74 people, including players and officials, were interviewed. Within three months he produced a written report, which was published by the ACB.

The inquiry was not open to the public and it did not enjoy the protection of legal privilege. Although this has been criticised, the ACB believed that some people would be more forthcoming in such a private inquiry. When the findings were announced, however, some of the important information was hidden in a 'confidential chapter' – for the ACB's eyes only.

But the report told enough to leave lots of food for thought. During Australia's tour to India in 1992, a 'retired Indian cricketer' (identity as per the confidential chapter) approached Dean Jones, asking for information in return for payment. There were rumours that the 1992 match between a World XI and an Indian XI was fixed. During Australia's tour to England in 1993, captain Allan Border was approached by 'a former Pakistan cricketer' and offered money to lose the final test of the series. During Australia's 1994 tour to Sri Lanka and Pakistan, the association of Mark Waugh and Shane Warne with a bookmaker named John, began. In 1997 Ricky Ponting was approached by a bookmaker at a greyhound meeting in Sydney, asking for information in return for payment. And during Australia's 1998 tour to Pakistan, Mark Taylor was approached to provide information.

Of significance was the fact that the 1992 offer to Dean Jones, as well as the 1993 offer to Allan Border, was not mentioned in the tour manager's report. The importance of this lesson, as posted on the internet, was that the official tour reports cannot always be considered to be a full record of what had happened on previous tours. Questions, therefore, need to be asked by cricket administrators about such tours going back in history; especially those tours that seem to be rife with rumours.

There was another very significant lesson in the O'Regan report. This time, it related to John, the bookmaker who received information from Mark Waugh and Shane Warne.

The report stated the following: 'The bookmaker indicated to Mark Waugh that he had players from around the world in various international cricket teams providing him with information.' This is quite a sweeping statement. Were South African players questioned in this regard at the time?

A year later, Hansie Cronjé told the King Commission about the approach by 'an Indian or Pakistani man, who described himself only as "John"', in January 1995 (this was the Mandela Trophy approach, first alluded to by Pat Symcox). Cronjé, himself, went on to say that he believed this might be the same individual referred to in the ACB hearings.

The O'Regan report also drew important conclusions about the way that bookmakers operated. Notably, it pointed out that somebody who had accepted money 'for apparently harmless information' might be considered likely to 'succumb to more serious financial inducements'.

Furthermore, the telephone communication with players close to and before games, was highlighted as one of four key factors prevalent in both the 1992 offer to Dean Jones and the 1994 approach to Shane Warne and Mark Waugh.

The final lesson to be learnt from the O'Regan report was that approaches and incidents were taking place on a consistent basis throughout the 1990s. This raises question marks over the large time-gaps during which no prospective transgressions in South Africa have been uncovered in the King Commission – notably the three-year period from 1997 to 2000.

The O'Regan report culminated in a set of recommendations. One of them was that the ACB Code should be amended to include a rule in terms of which the provision of information by a player is prohibited.

But the O'Regan report never featured during the first round of the King Commission.

Lessons from another sport

One of the most famous incidents of match-fixing in sport took place as long ago as 1919, when eight infamous players in the Chicago White Sox baseball team conspired to throw the 1919 World Series. Because of this, the team was subsequently referred to as the Black Sox. Numerous books have been written about the affair, but perhaps none as revealing as *Eight Men Out*, by Eliot Asinof.

Change the names, the dates and the places (and, of course, the small matter of the actual sport), and you have all the ingredients that produced the Hansie Cronjé affair some eighty years later. The characters and their motives are all the same; the only unpredictable part is the final outcome.

But the point is that the truth of the matter was never discovered during the lifetimes of those players. It was only established four to five decades later, with the deaths of certain key individuals. No wonder then, that the first edition of *Eight Men Out* was only published in 1963, forty-four years after the scandal itself took place.

Eight Men Out describes the fine balancing act between destroying a sport, either because one uncovers too little (and people are thus allowed to continue with their transgressions to the ultimate detriment of the game), or one uncovers too much (and the game suffers irreparable damage in the eye of the public, meaning less money for all concerned).

Extending this to the game of cricket in the present day, there is an argument that there are too many good people making an honest living from the game, that their livelihoods should be unfairly jeopardised by the dishonesty of the few. The sport, itself, is too important – it has to be protected. And this reasoning has probably been at the core of administrators around the world, dragging their feet in uncovering the full extent of corruption in the sport once and for all.

The sad truth is also that there is only ever one group of winners in these betting scandals, namely those who control the scam for their own financial gain. They were never exposed in the Black Sox scandal. Those who suffered most were the players involved, as their brilliance did not extend beyond the baseball field. Banned from the one activity at which they were supremely good, their lives were reduced to the mundane. Nor did they ever escape the shadow of their shame. Worse still, was that the single player most remembered from this affair, and the one who lost the most because he was the most talented – Shoeless Joe Jackson – was probably the one player who was never involved.

In an anecdote which is as sad as it's famous, there was a tearful boy who grasped Jackson by the arm, on his way out of the courtroom. 'Say it ain't so, Joe!' the boy begged, repeatedly. (*Say it ain't so, Joe!* would eventually become the title of another book written about the affair, this time an attempt specifically to clear Jackson's name, published in 1979.) How much more succinctly can one summarise the tremendous impact that a fallen idol, like Hansie Cronjé, has on scores of schoolboy fans?

The opponents of the Chicago White Sox in the 1919 World Series were the Cincinnati Reds.

At the same time that *Eight Men Out* was published, in 1963, a 22-year-old rookie joined the very same Cincinnati Reds. His name was Pete Rose, and he would go on to become baseball's all-time hit leader. This was in spite of the fact that Rose was generally considered not to be a natural, and he had to work harder than most other players in order to achieve.

But Pete Rose also had one fundamental flaw: he was a compulsive gambler. Although never admitting that he'd actually bet on a game of baseball, Rose was eventually suspended from the sport; he also ended up serving a prison sentence.

Pete Rose's fall from grace was considered to be a national disaster by many Americans. He had, after all, been one of baseball's most famous players.

Yet, the sport has gone from strength to strength ever since. There's a lesson in this, itself.

Lessons for the fans

Thomas Carlyle was a nineteenth-century Scottish philosopher. He published a defining work entitled *On Heroes, Hero-Worship, and the Heroic in History* way back in 1841.

In a collection of six lectures, Carlyle describes the different types of heroes who played a part in his Victorian world. Exploring Scandinavian mythology, he begins with a look at the hero as divinity. He proceeds to look at the hero as prophet, explaining the role of Mohammed. He then looks into the hero as poet, and analyses the contribution of Dante and Shakespeare. He further describes the hero as priest, focusing on Martin Luther and John Knox. He also examines the hero as man of letters, with reference to Johnson, Rousseau and Burns. And he concludes with the hero as king, closing off with a discussion about Napoleon.

No doubt Carlyle would have included the hero as sports star if he had lived 150 years later. For the one thing that is true about every Great Man, according to Carlyle, is that 'He is the living light-fountain, which it is good and pleasant to be near'.

And that is exactly the kind of role that we expect our heroes to play for us, as we exist from day to day in a society that surfs the internet and watches twenty-four-hour sports channels on satellite television. Every day we invite these heroes into our lives, and we invite them into our homes.

The extent of hero-worshipping, practised by somebody, is typically a function of the success and the excitement contained in the individual's own life – or rather the lack thereof. The less the quality of life of the individual, the more he or she needs to live vicariously through the experience and the achievements of others.

That is why the Royal Family has a following: not because millions of citizens want to be loyal subjects, but because so many people subconsciously wish that they could have the fairytale life of the King or the Princess.

And that is why we, and the press, our official mouthpiece, build up our sports heroes in the way that we do. We build them up because they might actually achieve what we can only ever aspire to do. And we build them up to such dizzy heights that they can eventually only tumble, whether through loss of form, or losing their way.

The diverse reactions of different people to the news of the Hansie Cronjé scandal were interesting to analyse. Many were angry. 'How could Hansie do it? How could he let all of us down like that?'

There were many different reasons for people's anger. There were the thousands of parents, angry because it was now up to them to explain the situation to young children who had life-size pictures of the South African captain on their walls. There were large businesses that had to scramble in order to put an end to endorsement arrangements and advertising campaigns that included the idol's name or image.

And there would, of course, be scores of people who were angry for their very own, personal reasons. On a visit to London, I spoke to an Afrikaner lady whose family had emigrated to England many years ago. Her husband was a successful businessman; she was a housewife. She told me how she had battled, for many years, to adapt to the English way of life. She told me how difficult it was for her to make friends. Basically, she told me about the social inferiority complex from which expatriates often suffer in a sophisticated, foreign environment. But then Hansie Cronjé appeared on the scene. He was an Afrikaner like herself, his accent sounded like her own, yet he was good enough to compete on a world stage. Even better: he was good enough to lead his team to glorious victories over the English team; the very English who would never allow her to feel completely at home in their country. Needless to say, he became her ultimate hero. He rescued her from a backwater identity and gave her the confidence simply to be herself. Until he was found out to be less than honest. If this was the real Hansie, then who was she? She retreated back into her shell.

Others were sad. 'How could something like this ever happen to somebody like Hansie?'

And sadness quickly translates into forgiveness. Because the more quickly we forgive somebody we love, the more quickly we are able to forget the sadness brought on by what he, or she, has done wrong in the first place. And for many people it is easier to forgive the fallen hero (for what he had done wrong) than it is to forgive themselves (for the fact that they had made an inappropriate choice of hero, in the first instance).

Once again, there were many people who simply forgave Hansie for very personal reasons. Once, I went out to lunch with an acquaintance who had separated from his wife after admitting to an adulterous affair. I only mention this trivial bit of detail because I believe it is one hundred percent relevant to the way that his opinion was formed, relating to the question of what should now be Hansie Cronjé's fate. According to him, Hansie had done the honourable thing by coming clean. He had faced the consequences and he now deserved another chance; not only to get on with his life but, in fact, to play cricket again and to captain his country.

Some were joyful. 'See, I told you so. He's not so great, after all!' This would obviously include many of the people who were never fans in the first place. But it also represents the flip side of the hero-worshipping argument, previously put forward. To start with, heroes make us feel better about ourselves because they represent our aspirations. And when they end up failing morally, we can feel better about ourselves once more, because at least we know that there is now one area in which we are superior to the heroes themselves!

Perhaps the best reaction, however, is not to become too emotional about the life of a sports star, or any other hero for that matter, with whom you never had any personal relationship in the first place.

Heroes come and heroes go, but no individual will ever be bigger than the sport. And in the same way that most monuments, erected in honour of politicians in their own lifetimes, are the ones that are broken down in subsequent eras, so we should take care not to overdo the way in which we idolise our sports heroes prematurely.

Records should be admired, not people.

Admire those people who set the records if you want to, but don't expect them to be something which they simply cannot be. In the final instance, they are only human.

Concluding remarks

What does the future hold for Hansie Cronjé?

First and foremost, the answer to this depends on the findings of the King Commission. If the judge rules that he made a full declaration of his wrongdoings and that he was honest and truthful in every aspect, he will get indemnity from prosecution in his home country.

Even if he does not get indemnity, however, it is not clear what the grounds may be for any possible prosecution. Legal opinion is divided as to whether South African anticorruption laws apply to the circumstances in the Cronjé case.

Regardless of the King Commission's findings, however, there is a separate judicial process taking place in India. For how long will Hansie Cronjé be a wanted man in that country? And how conclusive is their evidence? Or will Cronjé get away with the explanation that he did nothing wrong in India ... that he was merely 'spinning them along'?

There is also likely to be a disciplinary process under the auspices of the UCBSA. Hansie Cronjé has already announced that he has cut his ties with 'representative' cricket. This seems to suggest, however, that he's leaving himself a backdoor to potentially become involved in the sport again, whether as coach, administrator or otherwise. But ultimately, the UCBSA is empowered to rule in that regard.

Tough new measures to stamp out corruption in cricket have been announced at the ICC level. And Hansie Cronjé, himself, has already admitted to some serious transgressions. Put these two points together, and it is to be expected that South Africa's cricket authorities may feel obliged to make an example out of Cronjé and impose a lifelong ban from all involvement in the sport. If this happens, it can literally mean that he may never be able to coach the third team of the local primary school again, as that school will be affiliated to a provincial body which, in turn, will fall under the ultimate auspices of the UCBSA.

Can the UCBSA go further than imposing a life ban on Hansie Cronjé?

Theoretically, yes. As somebody who used to play the sport at representative level, his situation is covered by exactly the same rules and regulations as those that Herschelle Gibbs's disciplinary hearings were based on. This means that, like Gibbs, Cronjé can also be given a monetary fine.

But can they force Cronjé to pay? In the Gibbs case, it's easy: of course he'll pay, because he wants to play cricket again. In fact, the fine could always be deducted from his next pay cheque, or two. The same does not, however, apply to Cronjé. So, if they fined him and he neglected to pay, the UCBSA would have to institute civil proceedings, and they could probably do without that kind of publicity. There is, after all, a difference between a one-sided disciplinary hearing and a two-sided civil action. And we already know that the relationship between the UCBSA and Hansie Cronjé was less than perfect ...

* * * * *

The most important question, however, is how much more there may be to find out about corruption in South African cricket. Only time will tell.

In the meantime, we can only hope that every run that is scored by our team represents a commitment to victory, and every catch that is dropped is an honest attempt, nonetheless.

* * * * *

'Innocence is precious, but truth is better.'
(*Eight Men Out,* by Eliot Asinof)

Acknowledgements

Writing a book like this is a great deal of fun, but it would most certainly be a lot less fun if one did not receive assistance from those around you.

Kelvin Watt was a great help and inspiration. Yes, he nearly did kill himself laughing when first I told him about the book. But, as luck would have it, he was actually spending the evening at Graham Ford's place in Durban when I reached him on his cellphone that first time – I couldn't help but think that had to be a positive omen. No doubt, without his encouragement and contacts, the book would not have gotten off the ground.

François Pienaar was extremely generous, not only in contributing the introduction to this book and sharing his considerable experience of the publishing world with me, but also with his and Nerine's wonderful hospitality one beautiful day in London.

Of all the people interviewed, none was as cooperative and forthcoming as Tim Noakes. As a runner, I have been a fan of the doctor and his books for many years. To meet him and chat with him was a privilege.

I expected a tough interview with Johan Volsteedt but I couldn't have been more wrong: he was warm and hospitable. He more than convinced me of his approach to cricket coaching which focuses not on the game, but on lessons for life. Educators like him are rare; Grey College is very fortunate to have him.

Kepler Wessels was direct as ever. His no-nonsense approach has served him well on the cricket field in a career that spanned more than two decades; today it makes him one of the most valuable contributors in the world of cricket journalism.

Imtiaz Patel will never change: he had lots of stories and an abundance of humour every time we met. It's a telling blow for cricket that his talents are now deployed elsewhere.

It was an unforgettable experience to meet Pastor Ray McCauley; I appreciate the time he afforded me in a busy schedule filled with meetings, speaking engagements and overseas travels.

Graham Ford agreed to see me under difficult circumstances, a couple of days before the national team left for Sri Lanka. Craig Matthews was generous with his time and his stories. It was great to spend quality time with Richard Snell in Johannesburg on a number of different occasions. Craig Smith was most accommodating and was able to cite some very interesting facts and figures. If you thought these looked like nice guys when watching them on television, believe me, they're even nicer when you deal with them in person.

There have been countless newspaper articles about the Hansie Cronjé affair. To this day, I believe the most entertaining piece of journalism has been Max du Preez's article, reproduced with kind permission in the chapter, 'The Afrikaner connection'. I am flattered to be able to use it. I still haven't met Max, but we've built up an e-mail friendship second to none.

Rian Botes is not only an exceptional sports photographer, but he is also very knowledgeable about the game of cricket. And he's a great guy to do business with.

For those cricket fans that haven't yet found it out for themselves, the amount of stuff about the sport that you can access on the internet is absolutely mind-boggling. *Cricinfo.com* is particularly useful: I was able to access scorecards of matches going back decades on the site. It also houses more insightful articles than any cricket fan can wade through in a lifetime.

Mweb.co.za and its close cousin *news24.co.za* were further great internet sources. The video streaming of Hansie's testimony on *M-Web* turned this sceptic into a technology convert forever. The full transcripts of the King Commission, also available on this site, came in more than handy.

Charles de Kock, my 'boss' at Old Mutual Asset Managers (inverted commas because we'd like to believe that we've got a pretty flat structure at OMAM), was tremendous when I presented him with a rather unconventional management issue. Tim Cumming was also most supportive.

Sydney Gregan read draft after draft of the book and made many valuable suggestions. For years he's been quoting Aristotle, telling me about the three things a man needs to do in life: plant a tree, father a child and write a book. One down, two to go.

When I walked into the office of Marlene Fryer at Zebra Press/Struik Publishers, I just knew that I'd struck on a winning partnership. Here was I, part-time writer with hope in abundance but zero track record, yet her approach was welcoming, accommodating and above all, totally professional. Over the next two months she remained excited yet patient; focused yet full of fun. From a timing perspective, she made the impossible happen – I am very much indebted to her. Thank you also to Kerryn McKay.

For ideas, opinions, referrals, assistance and general encouragement I am indebted to family, friends and colleagues aplenty. In particular I would like to thank my brother Gert, my sister-in-law Inge, Herman Bosman, Riaan Winter, Anthonie de Beer, Derik Coetzer, André Cronjé (no relation), Annalie Watt, Myron Zlotnick, Helmut Engelbrecht, Charl du Toit, Arnold Shapiro, Kokkie Kooyman, George Howard, Omri Thomas, Sello Moloko, Jeremy Bolton, Tanya Goussard, Arjan Buikema, Peter Baird, Nicol Stassen, James du Preez, Francois Gouws, Ryan Baskir, and James Twyman. Thank you also to M-Net's research department.

And of course, my two great friends in Cape Town, Richard Pitt and Fofo van der Merwe, who, by spilling the beans slightly prematurely (in separate conversations), made absolutely sure that there could be no turning back with the project. Thanks, guys.

Acknowledgements

Appendix

Hansie Cronje – Career Statistics
(compiled by P.J. le Grange & K-P. Munch, Precise Computing CC)

Domestic and first-class record: Batting

	M	I	NO	Runs	HS	Ave	100	50
Domestic first class	53	100	10	3765	161*	41.83	12	16
Tests	68	111	9	3714	135	36.41	6	23
All first class	184	310	33	12103	251	43.69	32	57
One-day internationals	188	175	31	5565	112	38.64	2	39
Domestic limited-overs night series	56	52	9	1802	120	41.9	4	13

Domestic and first-class record: Bowling & Fielding

	O	M	R	W	Ave	Best	RpO	SR	Ct
Domestic first class	382.5	98	1054	28	37.64	2/30	2.75	82.03	42
Tests	633.1	243	1288	43	29.95	3/14	2.03	88.35	33
All first class	1649	–	3995	116	34.43	4/47	2.42	85.32	121
One-day internationals	892.2	32	3966	114	34.78	5/32	4.44	46.96	74
Domestic limited-overs night series	154.5	8	675	24	28.12	3/26	4.35	38.71	15

Tests: Performances against all opponents (batting)

Opponent	M	I	NO	Runs	HS	Av'ge	100	50
Australia	12	21	1	788	122	39.10	1	6
England	18	26	2	706	126	29.41	1	4
India	11	21	2	524	135	27.57	1	1
New Zealand	7	9	1	471	112	58.87	2	2
Pakistan	6	10	1	299	85	33.22	-	2
Sri Lanka	5	9	1	452	122	56.50	1	3
West Indies	6	11	0	291	58	26.45	-	2
Zimbabwe	3	4	1	183	64	61.00	-	3
TOTAL	68	111	9	3714	135	36.41	6	23

ODI's: Performances against all opponents (batting)

Opponent	M	I	NO	Runs	HS	Av'ge	100	50
Australia	39	36	7	1364	112	47.03	2	9
England	22	22	1	667	78	31.76	-	4
Holland	1	1	0	41	41	41.00	-	-
India	34	31	10	909	90	43.28	-	6
Kenya	3	2	1	65	63*	65.00	-	1
New Zealand	20	19	3	543	78	33.93	-	4
Pakistan	24	21	3	696	81	38,66	-	5
Sri Lanka	15	14	0	243	50	17.35	-	1
UAE	1	1	0	57	57	57.00	-	1
West Indies	17	17	1	616	94	38.50	-	5
Zimbabwe	12	11	5	364	87*	60.66	-	3
TOTAL	188	175	31	5565	112	38.64	2	39

'... and nothing but the truth'?

Tests: Performances against all opponents (bowling)

Opponent	O	M	R	W	Av'ge	Best	RpO	SR
Australia	117.4	36	247	5	49.4	2/21	2.09	141.20
England	130	54	259	3	86.33	2/5	1.99	260.00
India	174.1	75	316	14	22.57	3/23	1.81	74.64
New Zealand	80.1	34	176	4	44.00	2/48	2.19	120.25
Pakistan	37.4	11	102	4	25.50	2/6	2.70	56.50
Sri Lanka	61.3	25	98	6	16.33	3/21	1.59	61.50
West Indies	17.1	5	53	3	17.66	3/19	3.08	34.33
Zimbabwe	14.5	3	37	4	9.25	3/14	2.49	22.25
TOTAL	633.1	243	1288	43	29.95	3/14	2.03	88.35

ODI's: Performances against all opponents (bowling)

Opponent	O	M	R	W	Av'ge	Best	RpO	SR
Australia	189.3	12	879	16	54.93	2/15	4.63	71.06
England	95.3	1	409	8	51.12	2/43	4.28	71.62
Holland	3	1	3	0	-	-	1.00	-
India	179	4	782	20	39.10	5/32	4.36	53.70
Kenya	5	0	26	2	13.00	1/5	5.20	15.00
New Zealand	72	1	397	9	44.11	3/26	5.51	48.00
Pakistan	126.5	5	512	15	34.13	2/17	4.03	50.73
Sri Lanka	76.4	3	328	11	29.81	2/21	4.27	41.81
UAE	4	0	17	0	-	-	4.25	-
West Indies	84	4	387	19	20.36	3/10	4.60	26.52
Zimbabwe	56.5	1	226	14	16.14	4/33	3.97	24.36
TOTAL	892.2	32	3966	114	34.78	5/32	4.44	46.96

Bibliography

Asinof, E., *Eight Men Out - the Black Sox and the 1919 World Series* (Henry Holt and Company, New York, 1963)

Australian Cricket Board, *The O'Regan Player Conduct Inquiry Report* (1998)

Beyers, C.J., *Dictionary of South African Biography, Volume 4* (Butterworths, Durban, 1981)

Carlyle, T., *On Heroes, Hero-Worship and the Heroic in History* (University of Nebraska Press, Lincoln, 1966)

Clingman, S., *Bram Fischer - Afrikaner Revolutionary* (David Philip Publishers, Cape Town, 1998)

Commission of Inquiry into Cricket Match Fixing and Related Matters (Commission established by the President in terms of Section 84(2)(f) of the Constitution of the Republic of South Africa (Act No 108 of 1996))

Donald, A., *White Lightning. Allan Donald - The Autobiography* (Harper Collins Publishers, London 1999)

Drucker, P.F., *Management Challenges for the 21st Century* (Butterworth Heinemann, Oxford, 1999)

Griffiths, E., *Kepler - The Biography* (Pelham Books, London, 1994)

Gropman, D., *Say It Ain't So Joe - The True Story of Shoeless Joe Jackson* (Carol Publishing Group, Secaucus, N.J., 1992)

Hartman, R., *A Year on ... Hansie and the boys* (New Holland Struik, Halfway House, 1998)

King, E.L., *Interim Report of the Commission of Inquiry into Cricket Match Fixing and Related Matters* (Cape Town, 2000)

Lambert, D., *Collins Gem Body Language* (Harper Collins Publishers, Glasgow, 1999)

Magazine, P., *Not Quite Cricket - The Explosive Story of How Bookmakers Influence the Game Today* (Penguin Books, New Delhi, 1999)

Mandela, N.R., *Long Walk to Freedom - The Autobiography of Nelson Mandela* (Macdonald Purnell, Randburg, 1994)

Morris, D., *Manwatching: A Field Guide to Human Behaviour* (Collins Publishing, London, 1987)

Morwood, J., (ed.), *The Oxford Latin Minidictionary* (Oxford University Press, Oxford, 1995)

Noakes, T., *Lore of Running* (Oxford University Press, Cape Town, 1985)

Sokolove, M.Y., *Hustle - The Myth, Life, and Lies of Pete Rose* (Simon & Schuster, New York, 1990)

Welsh, F., *A History of South Africa* (Harper Collins Publishers, London, 1998)

Wessels, K.C., *Cricket Madness* (Aandblom Publishers, Port Elizabeth, 1987)

Whales, C. (ed.), *Hansie: This is Your Captain Speaking* (Struik Publishing, Cape Town 1997)

Woolmer, B. (with Tennant, I.), *Woolmer on Cricket* (Virgin Publishing, London, 2000)